how2become

MEDICAL INTERVIEW QUESTIONS AND ANSWERS

by Richard McMunn

Orders: Please contact How2become Ltd, Suite 2, 50 Churchill Square Business Centre, Kings Hill, Kent ME19 4YU.

You can order further copies of this title through Amazon.co.uk, Gardners.com or directly through How2Become.com via the e-mail address info@how2become.co.uk.

ISBN: 978-1909229846

First published 2014

Typeset for How2become Ltd by Anton Pshinka.

Printed in Great Britain for How2become Ltd by: CMP (uk) Limited, Poole, Dorset.

CONTENT

WELCOME

Dear sir/madam,

I have created this guide to help you pass your medical interview. The guide is applicable to both those people who already work within the medical profession, and those who are seeking to get in to medical school and are required to sit an interview as a result.

Competition right now for jobs within this industry is fierce; therefore, you need to be at your best. Within this book I have provided you with a large number of interview questions, tips on how to respond to those interview questions and also a large number of sample responses to help you prepare fully. Within this book I have also provided you with some invaluable tips on how to predict the types of questions you are likely to get asked at a medical interview. If you know what the interview questions are likely to be, then your chances of success will increase greatly.

If you would like any further assistance with your preparation then we offer a wide range of products and training courses at the website www.how2become.com.

Finally, you won't achieve much in life without hard work, determination and perseverance. Work hard, stay focused and be what you want!

Good luck and best wishes,

The how2become team

The How2become team

PREFACE BY AUTHOR RICHARD MCMUNN

For the vast majority of people, interviews are a nerve-wracking experience. At the very least, they are something that you could probably do without. This book aims to change your entire mind-set towards your medical interview and more importantly, making you believe that success is in your own hands.

I have enjoyed a fantastic career during my life so far. I have been an Aircraft Engineer in the Royal Navy, an Officer in the Fire Service and now an award-winning entrepreneur and best-selling published author. I left school with very few qualifications, but I was determined not to let my lack of educational achievement get in the way of being successful.

During my time in the Fire Service I passed many promotional interviews. I was successful at over 95% of interviews that I attended. My success wasn't down to luck, or some miracle 'interview success gene', but rather adopting the correct approach to both my interview preparation and also the interview itself. During this guide I will teach you how to implement my success formula so that you achieve the highest scores possible during your medical interview.

The majority of people believe that you have to answer every interview question correctly in order to get the job. This couldn't be further from the truth. Yes, it is important to demonstrate during your medical interview that you have both the subject knowledge of the role you are applying for, and also knowledge about the organisation you are applying to join, but it is just as important to work on your interview technique and your 'likeability' factor. When I interview people for roles within my company I will put more emphasis on a candidate's likeability factor rather than on their technical ability and their ability to respond to the questions. I am not saying that you should neglect these important areas, far from it. What I am saying, though, is that you should portray yourself in a positive and enthusiastic manner during the medical interview, simply because teamwork and the ability to work with others within the medical professional are absolutely vital. If you follow my advice and prepare fully, then your chances of success will improve.

What is the likeability factor?

The likeability factor could involve some or all of the following:

- Being polite and courteous at the interview.
- Displaying respect and good manners, i.e. not sitting down in the

interview chair until invited to do so by the panel.

- Showing a high level of enthusiasm for the job you are being interviewed for.
- Taking a pride in your appearance.
- Showing a willingness to go above and beyond the minimum expectations.

When I prepare for any interview I will always split my preparation up into three different areas, and I want you to do the same. These are:

- Interview technique
- Research
- Predicting and responding to the interview questions

If I work on all of these three elements in equal measures then I will have the confidence and knowledge to pass the interview. When I walk through that door into the interview room I only have one thing on my mind – impressing the panel sufficiently that they will have to give me the job. During this guide I will teach you how to comprehensively cover all three of these areas.

So, you will probably be able to tell that my mind-set, both prior and during the interview, is one of confidence and self-belief. These two factors are very important in helping you to pass the medical interview. By the time you've finished reading this guide you will have both confidence and self-belief in abundance.

I strongly believe that passing interviews is like riding a bike – once you know how, it never leaves you. Take the time to study the contents of this guide and then go and pass your medical interview with flying colours!

Best wishes,

Richard McMunn

CHAPTER 1
INTRODUCTION

INTRODUCTION

Medical organisations are seeking people who are confident, reliable, enthusiastic, knowledgeable, flexible, motivated, hard-working, committed and loyal. By understanding what an interview panel are looking for in a successful candidate, you will be increasing your chances of success dramatically. Before I go into any interview I always try to put myself in the shoes of the interviewer. What are they looking for in an employee, what are the key qualities required to perform the role, and what does the job description say? Once I have the answer to these questions then I can start to prepare effectively for the interview.

What is a medical interview?

A medical interview is a tool used by the employer to assess your potential to perform the role you have applied for. Unless you are an internal applicant who is seeking a promotion or sideways move, the interview will normally be the first time that the employer has the opportunity to meet you face-to-face. They will want to assess whether or not you have the qualities to perform the role competently, the experience that you have so far in a similar role, and also whether they like you as a person and whether you are likely to fit into their team environment. Remember, the ability to work effectively as part of a team is crucial to the success of the medical organisation you are applying to work for.

A job interview is your opportunity to shine. It is your chance to show the employer that you are the person for the job and that you will do all that you can to perform above and beyond expectations, if successful. Just by being at the interview you should naturally be enthusiastic about the prospect of working for the organisation. Why be there, if your heart is not in it?

The psychological element of a medical interview is very important. Preparing mentally and emotionally is just as important as researching the medical organisation. Being in the right mind-set will help you to perform at your best. There are many things that you can do to ensure you are in the right frame of mind, both immediately prior to the interview, and in the weeks and days leading up to it. Some of these include walking, running, swimming or general exercise, eating healthily and also avoiding alcohol or junk food. To the majority of people, these small changes won't seem worth the effort. However, through personal experience, these small changes can make a massive difference to your mind-set and self-confidence.

Matching the job description and/or the person specification

Before you start preparing for the medical interview I want you to get a copy of the job description and person specification for the actual job you are applying for. These will help us to ensure you are fully prepared.

The vast majority of medical organisations will assess you primarily against these important documents. Your first task is to identify areas where you match the job description and person specification for your chosen role. You will see on the following page that I have provided you with a sample job description for an Adult Nurse. Following the job description you will notice that I have provided you with a number of 'key evidence areas'. These areas are the ones that I suggest a candidate who is being interviewed for this post focuses on during his or her preparation. It is vital that you can provide **evidence** of where you match the job description for the role that you are applying for.

ADULT NURSE: JOB DESCRIPTION

Adult nurses care for adult patients who are suffering from acute and long-term illnesses and diseases. They support recovery from illness or operation by using care plans, carrying out care procedures and assessments and by focusing on the needs of the patient rather than the illness or condition. They also promote good health and well-being through education.

Nurses usually work within a multidisciplinary team but are the main point of contact for patients, often providing the most continuity of care. Adult nurses work mainly in hospitals and the community, attached to a health centre or general practice and in residential homes, specialist units, schools and hospices. Many nurses work with patients in their own homes.

Typical work activities

Gaining the trust and confidence of each patient is an important aspect of the job for nurses, especially as they have more contact with patients than other members of the medical team. This extends to developing a good relationship with the patient's relatives as well, particularly in cases of chronic illness where the patient may be returning regularly for treatment.

Patients may have chronic conditions, such as diabetes or heart/kidney problems, or serious acute conditions, such as heart failure, stroke, hepatitis or burns. They may be in hospital for surgery, admitted to accident and emergency with injuries, attending an outpatient clinic or undergoing tests and assessments.

The trend for community-based care has led to an increase in the number of opportunities for working in the community. By giving people preventative treatment and meeting patient needs in the comfort of their own home, unnecessary travel to hospital for appointments and hospital admissions is often avoided. It is possible for a newly qualified nurse to work in the community, although many gain a year's hospital experience first.

Exact duties may vary depending on your role but will usually include:

- writing patient care plans;
- implementing plans through tasks such as preparing patients for operations, wound treatment and monitoring pulse, blood pressure and temperature;
- observing and recording the condition of patients;
- checking and administering drugs and injections;
- setting up drips and blood transfusions;
- assisting with tests and evaluations;
- carrying out routine investigations;
- responding quickly to emergencies;
- planning discharges from hospital and liaising with community nurses, GPs and social workers;
- communicating with and relieving the anxiety of patients and their relatives;

- advocating on behalf of patients;
- educating patients about their health;
- organising staff and prioritising busy workloads;
- mentoring student and junior nurses;
- maintaining patient records;
- making ethical decisions related to consent and confidentiality.

Key evidence areas

Within this short section I will now provide you with sample 'key evidence areas' that are based on the sample Adult Nurse job description. This information will help you to understand the process I go through when coaching individuals to prepare for their medical interview. Although the key evidence areas are specifically based on the Adult Nurse role, you can use this exact same process for any job within the medical profession.

- Provide examples of where you have communicated effectively with a stressed or anxious relative. Make sure you provide details of how you communicated effectively by both speaking and listening. You should also explain how you focused on their needs at all times during the communication and demonstrated empathy.

- Give examples of where you have carried out routine tasks on a regular basis. During your response make sure you provide details of how you maintained concentration levels whilst carrying out any routine tasks, so as to minimise the risk of errors or mistakes.

- Provide one example of when you have responded effectively to an emergency situation. During your response be sure to provide details of how you followed your training and also applied the organisations policies and procedures for the emergency task you were undertaking. You should also provide details of how you maintained safety at all times during the situation or incident.

- Provide details of where you have successfully educated a patient or individual following concerns about their lifestyle or otherwise. Make sure you provide details of how you reinforced the educational message by providing them with literature or directing them to additional resources online.

- Provide evidence of where you have maintained confidentiality in a work-related situation.

- Provide evidence of where you have liaised with other stakeholders in order to improve the health or well-being of a patient. For example, this might be where you have passed on important information regarding a patient to community nurses, GPs and/or social workers. During your response you should provide details of how you ensured the message being passed was fully understood by the receiving party or person.

- Give an example of when you have created a patient care plan. During your response you will need to provide details of what you took into consideration whilst creating the plan.

Once you have listed all of the key evidence areas you will then be able to predict the interview questions. Here's how to do it.

How to predict the interview questions

Step 1 – Get a copy of the job description and person specification for the role you are applying for.

Step 2 – Grab a highlighter pen and 'highlight' the key evidence areas for the role.

Step 3 – You will now be able to predict the interview questions based on the key evidence areas. For example, according to the Adult Nurse Job Description we studied, one of the key requirements for the role is being capable of 'writing patient care plans'. The predicted interview questions for this particular evidence element are:

Q. Provide an example of where you have created and developed a patient care plan.

Q. What process would you go through when creating a patient care plan?

Q. What considerations would you take into account when creating a patient care plan?

By following the above process you will easily be able to predict the interview questions for the medical role you are applying for. In order to make it easier for you I will now provide a practical demonstration using a job description for a paediatric nurse. To begin with, take a look at the following job description.

PAEDIATRIC NURSE: JOB DESCRIPTION

Paediatric nurses assess, plan and provide nursing care for children who are suffering from a wide variety of conditions including diseases, illnesses and cancer or who are recovering from surgery.

Paediatric nurses work as part of a multidisciplinary team of professional and medical staff that includes doctors, health visitors, social workers, therapists and play workers. Many nurses work within the community, supporting families that are caring for sick children at home.

Typical responsibilities include:

- providing pre and post operation care
- monitoring and administering medication, injections, blood transfusions and intravenous infusions
- treating wounds
- taking patient samples, pulses, temperatures and blood pressures
- checking patients' conditions and monitoring functions such as respiration
- dealing with emergencies
- supervising junior staff
- organising workloads
- tutoring student nurses
- obtaining parental consent for treatment
- keeping accurate records
- writing reports
- providing information, emotional support and reassurance to patients and relatives
- ensuring adherence to strict hygiene and health and safety rules.

From the sample paediatric nurse job description I can predict the types of question I will get asked during the interview. Here's a list for you:

Q. Give an example of when you have written a complex patient care plan. What did you take into consideration whilst creating the plan?

Q. Can you provide a specific example of when you have followed health and safety rules during a work-related situation?

Q. How do you ensure that you keep accurate records on a day-to-day basis?

Q. How do you organise your working day to ensure you meet all of your targets and provide excellent patient care?

Q. Can you provide a specific example of when you have supervised a junior member of your team?

Q. Describe a time when you had to check a patients' condition? Please explain the process you followed and also any further care or treatment you recommended following the checks.

Q. Please provide details of when you have obtained a parental consent for treatment. How did you approach the situation/task and what did you consider?

Q. Can you give an example of when you tutored a student nurse? How did you approach the training and what did you consider at the time?

Q. Can you provide details of when you gave emotional support and reassurance to a relative of a sick patient? What did you take into consideration and why?

The above sample interview questions have been created by analysing the job description. I guarantee that at least 75% of the above questions will come up at the interview for this particular role in one format or another. So, the first step when preparing for your job interview is to get hold of a copy of the person specification and job description and start analysing them in order to predict some of the interview questions. Whilst there are other types of interview questions you will need to be prepared for during your medical interview, this process is a great starting point.

I will now go through a number of **basics** that you need to cover during your interview preparation. Whilst many appear obvious, please make sure you read them as they will all help towards achieving success at the medical interview.

Personal appearance

This carries far more weight than people think. First impressions are so important. It says a lot about who you are. Remember, you only get one opportunity to create a first impression. Unless it is specifically not required you should always dress in formal interview attire, such as a suit and tie or equivalent if you are female. Your shoes must be clean, too, and if you need a haircut, then get it done a few days before. I always advise people to prepare their interview clothes the night before the interview and lay everything out pressed, ironed and ready for the morning. The last thing you want to be doing is rushing around for your clothes or footwear on the big day only to find you threw away those smart shoes months ago. Be organised in your preparation!

Travelling to the interview

- How are you going to get to the interview?
- Do you know where you are going to park?
- Are the trains or buses running on time, if taking public transport?
- Do you need a congestion charge ticket if the interview is in London?

These are all obvious questions but important, nonetheless.

Again, it is all down to preparation. Remember to take a contact number with you just in case you are going to be late for the interview. Then you can call them well in advance to tell them you will be late due to a breakdown or traffic congestion. If you are travelling by car, don't wear your jacket. Hang it up on a coat hanger so that it is not creased when you arrive for the interview.

Punctuality

This can be related to the above subject but is still just as important. Make sure you leave with plenty of time to spare before your interview. It's far better to arrive an hour early than 5 minutes late. I usually arrive 30 minutes before my interview and sit in the car and re-read the job description for the role or information about the company that I am applying to join. If you are travelling by public transport, pull up a copy of the job description on your iPhone or smartphone and recap on the key areas of the document.

The interview format

Just by virtue of the fact you have been offered an interview indicates that the medical organisation believes you have the potential to work for them in that particular role. They will have already carried out a screening process based around the qualities and attributes relating to the post that you have applied for; this will have normally done at the application/CV stage. The interview is designed so that the employer can see you in person and look at your demeanour, presence, personality and appearance along with the opportunity to ask you questions based around your application, CV and the role that you are applying for. The basics of interview etiquette are key to your success, and you need to prepare for these as much as you do the interview questions themselves.

Most interviews will follow the following format:

Introduction and icebreaker

The interviewer should give you a brief overview of the interview and possibly the role that you are applying for. Dependant on the interviewer, you will be given the opportunity to tell the panel about yourself. Your response should be prepared beforehand and you can use this as an opportunity to sell yourself. You should cover brief topics relating to your experience, qualifications, passion for the job and your outside interests and ambitions. If you tell the panel that in your spare time you are working towards a qualification that can relate to the medical role you are applying for, then this can only be a good thing. Try to keep your introduction as brief as possible and don't go over two minutes in duration. Here's a sample introduction for you to read:

"My name is Jane and I have been working as an Adult Nurse for 7 years now. Prior to taking up my lifetime ambition of being a nurse, I worked as a sales assistant in a retail store. This job gave me some invaluable skills that I was able to transfer into the medical profession, namely the ability to work effectively as part of a team and also how to communicate effectively with the general public. I am extremely passionate about my work, but I do also have an active family and social life. I have two young children and a very supportive husband who helps out with childcare whenever I am working shifts. In my spare time I am currently studying for Diploma in Management as I eventually want to become a Ward Sister. I feel this qualification will assist me. I also enjoy playing badminton with friends once a week, shift patterns

permitting. I feel that maintaining a good level of fitness allows me to concentrate at work and help my employer deliver outstanding patient care. I would say that I am an energetic, passionate and trustworthy person who I believe would fit in very well to this new role that I am applying for."

The main interview (questions and answers)

This is the area in which you are asked a series of questions relating to your application, CV and the post that you have applied for. This is where you should do most of the talking, and if you have prepared well, you will be able to answer most questions, although it is not unusual to find yourself struggling to answer one or two. In this situation it is always best not to waffle. If you really don't know the answer to a particular question, just say.

The opportunity to ask questions

This is a time for you to ask questions of the panel. You should have two or three questions already prepared that you want to ask at the end. I have seen a few people fail interviews at this final stage. I can remember one particular person applying for a role as a firefighter. I was interviewing him for the role and he had answered all of the questions near perfectly. At the end of the interview I asked him whether he had any questions to ask the panel. Here's what he said:

"Yes I do have one question. How have I done? I personally think that I've had a fantastic interview and would I be very surprised if I've failed. Can I have feedback now please?"

The above question should never have been asked. It displayed arrogance and it also put the interview panel in an uneasy situation.

Make sure your questions are relevant but always avoid asking questions relating to leave or salary (unless you are specifically asked). Ask questions that relate to the role or development opportunities within the medical organisation you are applying to join. You may have researched the organisation and found that a new project is being developed. Ask them how the project is developing and what plans they have for the future. Don't ask questions where you are trying to be clever or questions that are too technical. If you try to catch them out they won't be impressed and they may come back and ask you a similarly difficult question.

Questions to ask

- If I am successful at interview, how long will it be before I could start in the new role? (This shows enthusiasm and motivation.)

- During my research I noticed that you recently opened a new sensory ward for patients with dementia. Has this been successful? (This shows a caring attitude towards the organisation, and also that you've carried out your research.)

- Even though I don't know yet whether I have been successful at interview, is there any literature I could read to find out more about the hospital? (This shows commitment.)

Questions to avoid

- How have I done during the interview? Have I passed? (This question demonstrates impatience and a slight level of arrogance. The interview panel will need to time to discuss your performance before making their decision.)

- How much leave will I get in this role? (I don't need to explain why this is a bad question!)

- How quickly can I progress through the company in terms of promotion? (This question, whilst demonstrating a level of enthusiasm, shows the panel that you have little intention of staying long in the role you have applied for.)

- I have a holiday booked in four weeks' time. If I am successful, can I have the time off? (You haven't even started in the role, and you are asking for time off. Wait until you have started in the role before discussing your leave requirements.)

The end of the interview

Make sure you remain positive at this stage and thank the entire panel for their time. This is a good opportunity to shake their hands. If you do shake their hand then make sure it's a firm grip and look them in the eye. There's nothing worse than shaking a person's hand when it feels like a wet lettuce!

At the end of every interview I recommend you leave the panel with a final statement. Here's an example:

"I just want to say thank you for inviting me along to interview. I've really enjoyed the experience and I have learnt a tremendous amount about your organisation. If I am successful then I promise you that I will work very hard in the role and I will do all that I can to deliver outstanding patient care and surpass your expectations."

This statement is very powerful. This is the final thing the interview panel will remember you for. When you leave the interview room they are probably going to asses/discuss your performance. Just as first impressions last, so too do final impressions.

CHAPTER 2
THE FORMULA FOR SUCCESS

THE FORMULA FOR SUCCESS

Over the last 20 years I have used the same formula time and time again to pass interviews. Over the next few pages and chapters I will explain what this formula involves, and more importantly how you can use it to assist you during your medical interview. The formula itself is a simple one, and is broken down into the following three different sections:

- Interview technique
- Research
- Responding to the interview questions

INTERVIEW TECHNIQUE

During your pre-interview preparation you must concentrate on developing your interview technique. This will involve concentrating on the following key areas:

- Creating a positive first impression
- Presentation
- Effective communication
- Body language and posture
- Asking questions
- Creating a positive final impression

Let's now break down each of these areas and look at them in detail.

Creating a positive first impression

An interview panel will naturally create a first impression of you. As soon as you walk into the interview room they will be forming an opinion. Therefore, it is important that you get off on the right foot. When you walk into the interview room, follow this process:

HOW TO CREATE A POSITIVE FIRST IMPRESSION AT YOUR MEDICAL INTERVIEW

Knock before you enter the room

↓

Walk into the interview room standing tall and smiling

↓

Stand by the interview chair and say "Hello, I'm [YOUR NAME], pleased to meet you."

↓

Shake the hand of each interviewer, whilst looking them in the eye

↓

Sit down in the interview chair, only when invited to do so

↓

Sit in the interview chair with an upright posture and with your hands resting palms facing downwards on the top of your knees, feet firmly on the floor

By following the above process you will be creating a positive first impression and demonstrating good qualities such as manners, self-discipline, politeness and motivation.

Presentation

Presentation effectively means how you intend to dress for the interview, and also how you intend to portray yourself. You want the interview panel to see you as a professional, motivated, conscientious and caring person who is taking the interview very seriously. For the interview make sure your outfit is cleaned and pressed, shoes polished and your personal hygiene is up to standard. This means simple things such as taking a shower, shaving, having a haircut and general grooming. You should also avoid brightly coloured clothes and generally go for a conservative approach such a dark blue, black or grey suit.

A good applicant

A good applicant is someone who has taken the time to prepare. They have researched both the medical organisation they are applying to join and also the role that they are being interviewed for. They may not know every detail about the organisation and the role but it will be clear that they have made an effort to find out important facts and information. They will be well presented at the interview and they will be confident, but not overconfident. As soon as they walk into the interview room they will be polite and courteous and they will sit down in the interview chair only when invited to do so. Throughout the interview they will sit upright in the chair and communicate in a positive manner, responding to the interview questions in a logical and structured manner, providing evidence when required. If they do not know the answer to a question they will say so and they won't try to waffle. At the end of the interview they will ask positive questions about the job or the organisation before offering a final positive statement and finally shaking hands and leaving.

A poor applicant

A poor applicant could be any combination of the following. They will be late for the interview or even forget to turn up at all. They will have made little effort to dress smartly and they will have carried out little or no preparation. When asked questions about the role they will have little or no knowledge and also offer no real evidence of the assessable qualities and attributes. During the interview they will appear to be unenthusiastic about the whole process and will look as if they want the interview to be over as soon as possible. Whilst sat in the interview chair they will slouch and fidget. At the end of the interview they will try to ask clever questions that are intended to impress the panel.

Improving interview technique

How you present yourself during the interview is important. Whilst assessing candidates for interviews I will not only assess their responses to the interview questions but I will also pay attention to the way they present themselves. A candidate could give excellent responses to the interview questions, but if they present themselves in a negative manner, this can lose them marks.

Effective communication

Effective communication is all about how you speak to the interview panel, and also how you listen to what they have to say. When responding to the interview questions you should speak clearly and concisely, avoiding all forms of waffle, abbreviations, slang or hesitations such as 'erm'. Look at each interview panel member when answering each question. Even though an interview question will be asked by one member of the panel at a time, you should always respond to the entire panel collectively. Look them in the eyes when speaking to them, but never stare them out. This will only portray you in an aggressive or confrontational manner. If you are unsure about a response to an interview question then just be honest. Consider saying something along the lines of:

"I'm sorry I do not know the answer to that question. I will look the answer up as soon as I get back home and contact you to let you know the answer."

If they accept this response, make sure you do research the response and contact them to let them know. When the interview panel are speaking to you, or if they are asking you a question, always demonstrate good listening skills. This means using positive facial expressions to show that you are taking on board what they are saying. Nod to show them that you understand the question(s) and smile when appropriate.

Body language and posture

Whilst sat in the interview always make a conscious effort to sit upright and not slouch. It is perfectly acceptable to use your hands to emphasise points when responding to the questions, but be careful not to overdo it. Even if the interview is going great and you are building up a good rapport with the panel, don't let your standards drop. Always maintain good body language and posture for the duration of the interview.

Final questions

Before you attend the interview think of two questions to ask the panel at the end. However, don't be trapped into thinking that you must ask questions. It is acceptable to say:

"Thank you but I don't have any questions. I have already carried out lots of research and you have answered some of my questions during the interview."

Some people believe that you must ask three, four or even five questions at the end of the interview – this is nonsense. Remember that the interview panel will have other people to interview and they will also need time to discuss your performance. If you do decide to ask questions then make sure they are relevant, as previously covered.

Creating a positive final impression

I have already discussed this during a previous section. I believe that a final positive statement can work wonders:

"I just want to say thank you for inviting me along to interview. I've really enjoyed the experience and I have learnt a tremendous amount about your organisation. If I am successful then I promise you that I will work very hard in the role and I will do all that I can to surpass your expectations."

RESEARCHING THE ROLE AND THE ORGANISATION

I highly recommend you visit the medical organisation or establishment you are applying to join prior to your interview. This serves a number of purposes. First of all it demonstrates a higher level of commitment and dedication than your competitors. Secondly, it will greatly assist you in your preparation.

Another great way to find out about the organisation is by visiting their website, if they have one. Look for their 'mission statement', 'goals or 'values' and learn them before your interview to understand what they are all about and where they are going in the future. Another effective research method is to type the company's name into a search engine such as Google or Bing. This should bring up a number of links for you to research. Make sure that the information you read is current and up-to- date, and don't waste time reading items that are more than a year old as you will most probably find that they have changed since then.

Topics you should research

You can spend many weeks studying different topics, but the following areas should be a priority in your research plan:

- Does the medical organisation you are being interviewed for, offer any development programmes for their members of staff, e.g. Investors in People?

- When were they established and what is their history?

- Is it a large company and do they have overseas interests? If so, what are those interests?

- Who is the Chief Executive and who are the shareholders? (Private sector)

- What are their short, medium and long-term goals?

- What are their values and policies?

- What type and level of care do they offer?

- Do they have a mission statement or vision? If so, what is it?

Top tip

Only research things that are relevant and don't waste time reading irrelevant articles. Use your time wisely.

You should also create an overview statement for the organisation you are applying to join or work at. An overview statement is basically a description of the organisation and what they do. This will enable you to answers questions such as:

Q. Tell me what you know about or organisation?

In order to assist you further during your preparation, here is a sample response to the above question for a candidate applying for a position within the Maidstone and Tunbridge Wells Trust.

"Maidstone and Tunbridge Wells Trust is an Acute Hospital Trust. This basically means that it provides a range of general hospital services from surgery and critical care, to emergency care and cancer services.

You currently care for approximately 500,000 people in the Maidstone and Tunbridge Wells area. The Trust employs approximately 4,000 staff in full time equivalent roles. You have a comprehensive training and development programme to ensure that all employees can realise their full potential.

The Trust operates from two primary sites. The first of your sites is the new state of the art Tunbridge Wells Hospital, which is the first all single room NHS hospital in England. The second is the excellent Maidstone Hospital. At Maidstone Hospital you have invested significantly in order to provide a new Cellular Pathology Centre, a stroke unit, a refurbished intensive care unit, state of the art CT and MRI scanners, a hi-tech operating theatre, a surgical training centre and a new birth centre.

Maidstone Hospital is also home to the Kent Oncology Centre, one of the leading cancer treatment centres in the southeast. Your cancer centre treats over 7,000 new patients a year from Kent and East Sussex, and was among the first nationally to benefit from a £4.7 million new treatment system that targets and treats tumours with pinpoint accuracy."

RESPONDING TO THE INTERVIEW QUESTIONS

The majority of medical interviews will contain two different types of questions. There will normally be motivational questions and situational questions. Here's an explanation for both sets of questions.

Motivational questions

Motivation interview questions are questions that are designed to assess the reasons why you want the role you have applied for, what you have to offer, how much research you have done and also why you are the best candidate for the job. Whilst they are relatively easy to prepare for, you should still spend plenty of time getting your responses ready to the perceived motivational interview questions as these can, and often do, catch people out. Here is a list of sample motivational interview questions.

Q. Tell us a about yourself.

Q. Talk me through your CV and personal statement.

Q. Why do you want this job?

Q. What do you have to offer?

Q. What skills do you have that would be of benefit in this role?

Q. Why should we give you the job and not the next candidate?

Q. I don't think you're experienced enough for this job. Convince me otherwise.

Q. What have you done to find out about this organisation and the role that you are applying for?

Q. How do you define success?

Q. What will you do if you are unsuccessful today?

You will see from the list that the questions are very much aimed at your 'motivation' for wanting to join their medical team. Before you attend the interview I would suggest that you prepare responses for all of these questions.

Situational questions

Situational interview questions are harder to respond to. In order to determine the type of situational interview question you could be asked, I recommend you get a copy of the person specification or job description for the role. Once you have this to hand, you will then be able to prepare responses to the type of situations that you will be expected to perform within the role. The key to scoring high during your responses to this type of questioning is to provide evidence of where you have already been in this type of situation.

To give you an idea of what a situational interview question looks like, I have compiled the following list.

Q. Give an example of where you have worked as part of a team to achieve a difficult goal or task.

Q. Give an example of where you have provided excellent patient care.

Q. Give an example of where you have dealt with a patient complaint. What did you do and say?

Q. Give an example of where you have carried out a routine medical procedure despite pressure from elsewhere.

Q. Give an example of where you have made a difficult decision despite objection from other people.

Q. Give an example of where you have taken on-board constructive criticism following a staff appraisal.

Q. Give an example of where you have dealt with a difficult or aggressive patient/visitor.

Q. Give an example of where you have resolved an issue with a work colleague.

I will now provide you with details of how to structure your responses to situational interview questions.

STAR method

The **STAR** method is one that I have used during my preparation for many interviews in the past. It works most effectively when preparing responses to situational type interview questions. I would certainly recommend that you use it when preparing for your medical interview.

The **STAR** method basically ensures that your responses to the interview questions follow a concise, logical sequence and that you also cover every possible area. Here's a breakdown of what the **STAR** method actually means:

Situation – At the commencement of my response to the interview question I will explain what the situation was and who was involved. This will be a relatively comprehensive explanation so that the interviewer fully understands what it is I am trying to explain.

Task – I will then explain what the task was. This will basically be an explanation of what had to be done and by whom.

Action – I will then move on and explain what action I specifically took, and also what action other people took in order to achieve the task.

Result – I will finally explain what the result was following my actions. It is important to make sure that the result was positive as a result of your actions.

Have a go at using the STAR method when creating responses to the interview questions that are contained within chapter 3. Write down the question at the top of a sheet of paper and write down each individual element underneath it. Now let's move on to the all-important sample interview questions and answers section of the guide. I have divided the interview questions into different chapters to assist you.

CHAPTER 3
GENERAL/WARM UP
INTERVIEW QUESTIONS

GENERAL/WARM UP INTERVIEW QUESTIONS

These types of questions are usually asked at the beginning of an interview. They are sometimes used by an interview panel to give you the opportunity to warm up in preparation for the assessable questions.

Q1 Tell me about you?

This question is very common during medical interviews and will probably be the first question they ask. When responding you should consider the following points:

- Provide a response that puts you across as a 'rounded' person. It is better to tell the panel about a variety of interests rather than just focusing on your work abilities and/or interests.

- If there is something interesting about you, tell the panel. This will stick in their mind, and when they come to score the interview, they will remember you for it. This might be something you have done for charity, a marathon you have run or some other type of achievement or award.

- Put yourself across in a positive light. Make the panel remember you for something that is interesting.

- Tell the panel about any qualifications you have or are currently working towards.

- You should also include a number of power words within your response which describe you as a positive person. Examples of power words include:

- Confident
- Enthusiastic
- Flexible
- Determined
- Caring
- Observant
- Committed
- Professional

Q2 Tell me about your CV. Talk me through it.

Questions relating to your CV are common during interviews of this nature. If you are applying for medical school then this question will focus on your personal statement as opposed to your CV. It is therefore important that you remember what you have included within your CV. Before you attend the interview have a read through your CV and make a mental note of its contents.

Consider the following points:

- Some people choose to be dishonest on their CV. Don't make the same mistake. Be honest at all times as you will get caught out at a later date if you are not.

- When responding to this question tell the panel about the salient points that are relevant to the job you are applying for. This may include experience, qualifications and personal qualities and attributes.

Q3 Why have you applied for this particular job?

Remember that an interview panel will have heard all of the usual responses to this type of question, such as "I've wanted to work in medicine since I was a young", and "This job just really appeals to me". These types of standard responses will gain few marks. It is crucial that you provide a response to this that is unique, truthful and different to all of the other candidates.

Consider the following points:

- Provide a response that demonstrates you've carried out plenty of research.

During your research something has caught your eye about the job that is appealing. This will demonstrate to the panel that you have looked into the role. Remember that some candidates will apply for many different medical jobs all at one time, and as a result they will fail to carry out any meaningful research.

- Consider providing a response that demonstrates you have the key skills required to perform the job competently. An example would be:

"I understand that this role requires very good communication and team working skills. I believe I am very strong in these areas, and therefore I would be a valuable asset to the team. Having researched the job and organisation extensively I have noticed a common theme appearing time and time again; professionalism.

I have also spoken to people who already work within this team, and the feedback I have received has been excellent.

I really want to work for this team and the skills and experience I have already gained will allow me to contribute towards the organisations goals in a positive manner".

CHAPTER 4

PERSONAL QUALITIES & ATTRIBUTES INTERVIEW QUESTIONS

PERSONAL QUALITIES & ATTRIBUTES INTERVIEWQUESTIONS

Questions that relate to your personal qualities are common during medical interviews. There are scores of questions that you could get asked around this subject heading and within this section we have provided you with the more common types. Prepare for each question thoroughly and also take note of the tips that are provided after each question.

Q4 What can you bring to this role?

Whilst it is a simple question, get it wrong and it could spell disaster for your chances of securing the job. When responding to this type of question you need to think about the core qualities that are required to do the job competently.

Consider the following points:

- Use keywords in your response such as - teamwork, communication skills, listening skills, enthusiasm, experience, commitment, flexibility, calm nature, driven, motivated, conscientious, hardworking, supportive, caring, compassionate, professional, competent, integrity etc.

Using keywords in your response to this type of question will put you across in a positive light. It will also give the panel something constructive to write down about you.

- When responding to this type of question it is far better to provide 'specific' examples of any experiences you have that directly relate to the role you are applying for.

Here follows a sample response to this question. Note how the candidate provides an example of 'positive achievement' within their response to demonstrate what they are capable of bringing to the role.

"Within this role I could bring a good level of knowledge, expertise and an ability to care for my patients. I would bring an ability to safely care for and treat my patients in a competent and professional manner, in line with the policies and procedures of the trust. I would work hard to achieve health and happiness for as many patients as possible. I know that I am capable of achieving this as I have already done this in my

current role. For example, within the last 6 months I have been praised no fewer than nine times on patient feedback forms that the hospital hands out following treatment and care of patients. I believe this feedback is representative of the level of care I provide and also my commitment to continuous professional development within my role."

Q5A. Describe yourself in 3 words.

This is not a common interview question, but one that can throw you if you are not prepared. Consider the following points:

- To prepare for this type of question, take a sheet of blank paper and write down 10 positive things about your character. These might be things that you personally feel you possess, or things that have been mentioned during previous appraisals.

- Now take a look at your sheet of paper and pick out 3 strong, positive words that stand out from the rest.

Consider the following 'positive' words. How do they make you feel?

- Dedicated
- Professional
- Trustworthy
- Motivated
- Enthusiastic
- Hardworking
- Careful
- Precise
- Conscientious
- Thorough
- Assertive
- Supportive

The above list contains just a few examples of character traits that inspire confidence in a person. Do any of them apply to you?

Q5B. What skills have you gained that would make you a good doctor/trainee?

The key to this question is that you need to provide skills that you already have, not ones that think you will have after you get the post. When responding to this type of question you need to follow these 3 simple steps:

Step 1 - take a look at the job description for the role you are applying for. What does it say about the skills that are needed to perform the role competently?

Step 2 - write down all of the skills you have gained so far in previous roles/training courses.

Step 3 - cross-match your skills with the ones that are required to perform the role competently. The ones that match are the ones that you need to provide in your response to the interview question.

To assist you, here are a few examples of skills that may help you within the medical profession.

- An ability to carry out my day-to-day work in an organised and methodical manner.
- An ability to work unsupervised.
- Able to respond to emergency or escalating situations.
- Capable of following medical and trust procedures whilst working under pressure.
- Able to create and maintain accurate patient records.
- A flexible approach to work.
- The ability to work as a competent team member.
- Able to remain calm and composed, especially whilst under pressure.
- Confident and resilient when required.
- Excellent timekeeping qualities.
- An ability to empathise when appropriate.

Q6. What do you think you would find challenging about this role?

This is a great interview question but it is one that can put you in an awkward position. To begin with, you do not want to come across as arrogant by saying that you wouldn't find anything challenging about the role, yet conversely you do not want to come across as if you would find everything challenging and wouldn't be able to cope. You need to find the right balance when answering this question.

Consider the following points:

- Think about the aspects of the job that are new to you, including ones that you have relatively little experience in. Now write them down. Once you have them down on paper, pick one that does not form part of the 'essential' criteria for the role or job description.

- Next, write down what skills or experience you have that you can use to counteract the area that you would find challenging, and use these skills when constructing your response. Let us now take a look at an example of how a candidate may respond to this interview question:

"As you can see from my CV, I have limited experience to date of dealing with patients. Whilst this could prove challenging for me, I have already taken steps to prepare for every eventuality. Over the last three months I have been shadowing a junior doctor on my ward. I have been watching carefully how he deals with his patients and I have learnt a tremendous amount which will help me to quickly become competent in this area. I have already proven in my previous roles that I have excellent communication skills, so whilst this will initially be a challenge, I have the skills to overcome this. I also thrive in a challenging environment, but if I was ever unsure, then I would always ask a senior doctor, consultant or manager for assistance."

Q7. How would your work colleagues describe you?

This is a relatively simple question to answer. Try to think of your own personal qualities and also what you have achieved at work over recent months and years. What skills and qualities were required to successfully accomplish your achievements? Now that you have these skills and qualities in your mind, write them down. You can be almost 100% certain that your work colleagues would agree with these skills and qualities.

When responding to this type of question it may also be wise to tell them something about you that you need to improve on. Nobody is perfect and if you just tell the panel glowing things about yourself they may think you are being arrogant. Be careful however as to what area of improvement you provide. A good example of an area of improvement that is cleverly turned around to be a strength could be:

"One area that my colleagues may say I need to improve upon is my patience. I can sometimes get impatient when people are late for a meeting or appointment. I pride myself on being punctual and some-times I expect the same from others when I shouldn't do. I am trying to work on this area however."

Whatever area of improvement you provide, make sure it isn't one that could do you any harm.

Q8. How would your patients describe you?

Again, this is a relatively easy question to answer. Before creating your response, take a look at the job description for the role that you are apply-ing for. What does it say about patient care and the standards the medical organisation or trust expects of its employees? Look for 'keywords' in the

Job description and then use them in your response.

Consider the following points:

- Patient care is very important. If you were a patient, what standard of care would you expect from your doctor or the nursing staff?

- Using positive keywords in your response can certainly help when re-sponding to questions of this nature. Examples of these include:

- Caring
- Efficient
- Sympathetic
- Organised
- Dedicated
- Conscientious
- Approachable
- Calm

Here is a sample response to help you:

"After speaking to some of my patients, and after reviewing patient feedback forms, I would say professional, caring and humorous. I am professional because I always put the needs of my patients first and foremost and carry out my duties diligently. I am caring because I take the time to build up a rapport with my patients and they feel they are being looked after by a doctor and team who genuinely want them to get better. I am humorous whenever possible because I think it brightens up a ward and also brightens up the patient's time in hospital, which can obviously be stressful and upsetting."

Q9. What made you decide to go into medicine?

Only you will know the answer to this question but consider the following points before creating your response:

- One of the qualities that separates an 'average' doctor/nurse from a 'good' doctor/nurse would have to be, in broad terms, his/her social and communication skills with the patients. This constitutes both verbal and non-verbal (body language) communication.

- When responding to this question, try to explain your strengths and how good you are at communicating with people and patients. You understand that one of the qualities a 'good' doctor or nurse has is his/her communication skills. You are a great communicator and therefore you wanted to go into a profession that would allow you to use these skills in order to help other people.

- Good responses to this type of question also include details of where the candidate enjoys being a 'role model' to other people. They decided they wanted to go into medicine so that they could have the opportunity to make a difference to others.

Q10. What are the qualities of a good doctor/nurse?

This question has been asked during both internal interviews and during medical school interviews. Once again, it would be wise to look at the job description and person specification for the post you are applying for before creating a response to the question. Within each of these documents you should be able to pick out a number of salient points with regards to the type of person they are looking for. This will be in addition to the standard qualities that a doctor or nurse would be expected to possess.

To demonstrate again how you can extract the expected 'qualities' from a person specification, take a look at the following job description for an adult nurse:

Sample job description - adult nurse

Adult nurses provide medical care and support the recovery of, patients suffering from acute and long-term illnesses, diseases such as diabetes or arthritis, or those requiring surgery. They focus on the needs of the patient rather than the illness or condition. They also promote good health and wellbeing through education. Nurses plan and carry out care within a multi-disciplinary team but are the main point of contact for patients.

Adult nurses work mainly in hospitals, although they are playing an increasingly prominent role in the community, attached to a health centre or general practice and in residential homes, specialist units, schools and hospices.

From the job description you will be able to find the following qualities:

- Caring.
- Supportive of patients.
- An ability to focus on the needs of the patient.
- Be capable of promoting good health through education.
- Have good organisational and planning skills.
- Community focused as and when required.

Q11. Tell us about the most influential person you have worked with to date. What did you like about him/her?

Questions of this nature are designed to test your awareness of the right skills and qualities that are required to do the job or role competently. For example, if whilst answering this question you informed the panel that you liked a work colleague because he or she were always telling jokes, then that might not impress the panel. Again, try to look at the job description and then think of a work colleague who has these qualities.

An example of how you may respond to this question could be:

"I remember working with a doctor at Coventry hospital about 4 years ago. He stuck in my mind because he was very different from the rest.

He was very professional, caring, organised and punctual. He always set an example to his peers and I always saw him as a role model of how things should be done. He also had an ability to make work colleagues and patients smile through his positive demeanour. He also had this fantastic ability to remain calm, regardless of much pressure he was under. I learnt a tremendous amount whilst working with him and his approach to work really taught me some good skills, which I have kept with me."

Q12. How do you organise your working day?

The reason why you are being asked this question is so the panel can identify how organised you are. When responding to this question it is crucial that you demonstrate an ability to organise your workload and prove that you can be relied upon to finish your work unsupervised.

Take a look at the following sample response to this type of question:

"I believe it is important to be organised in this job because other people, including patients and work colleagues, are depending on you to perform. Therefore, I always ensure I plan my day well in advance and I always keep my diary up to date. I also like to keep a list of what I aim to achieve on a particular day and this just acts as a reminder so that nothing is missed. If I have any appointments or meetings then I always make sure I arrive a few minutes early. I don't like to be late for anything as it is other people's time I am wasting and I avoid that as much as possible. I fully understand how important it is in this profession to be organised and I can be relied upon in this respect. I always spend five to ten minutes at the end of my shift planning the following day's activities. This enables me to get into the right mind-set before the start of shift as I have already been planning for my workload the day before."

Q13. What are your hobbies and how would you say they influence your medical career?

Getting the work life/personal life balance right, is important. If all you do is work, then at some point the stress will start to have a negative effect on both your work life, and also your personal/family life, too. Therefore, it is good to demonstrate that you have a hobby or interest that allows for a positive influence on your working career.

Generally, a medical career as either a doctor, nurse or otherwise can be stressful. Many people who have such stressful jobs try to counteract the effects of the stress through a hobby or interest such as running, cycling, pilates, yoga or other similar activity.

Take a look at the following response and you will notice how well it provides a positive effect on the respondents work life.

"In my spare time I love to walk my dog, go cycling and I also enjoy swimming. Apart from having a passion for the outdoors and fitness, it allows me to perform to a very high standard at work as my concentration and energy levels are always tip-top. In addition, my stress levels are always kept low due to my good level of fitness, so I find the pressures of work relatively easy to cope with. I always ensure that there's a healthy work and personal life balance which ultimately has a positive impact on my career."

Q14. Tell us about the worst work colleague or line manager that you have worked with to date. What did you dislike about them as a person or how they went about their work?

Be careful how you answer this question, and always make sure you separate personal conflicts from professional judgements. Always edge on the side of caution with these type of question and be tactful in your response.

Take a look at the following sample answer for some guidance on how you could structure your own response:

"I have rarely worked with anyone who has been unprofessional, however, on one occasion I did work with a doctor who had a very short fuse and he could react at the slightest thing. I remember being worried about his welfare on one occasion and I asked him if there was anything I could do to help. It transpired that he had problems at home, so we tried to get him some professional help to make things better for him.

If I was ever working with a colleague who was having a negative effect on the team then I would always try to see if I could help them in anyway. Sometimes a person's work performance can be influenced by external factors, which don't always necessarily help the wider team."

Q15. What are your weaknesses?

The opposite of this question would be "What are your strengths?", and one which is far easier to answer! Anyone who says they have no weaknesses is not telling the truth. We all have weaknesses but how you respond to this question is important. Consider the following points before creating your response:

- Try not to disclose a weakness that would have a detrimental effect on a team.

- Avoid weaknesses that are centred around trust, punctuality, competence or how organised you are. Always be truthful in your response but choose a weakness that will do you little harm.

- Explain to the panel that you are doing something about your weakness to make it better.

Take a look at the following response:

"Probably my biggest weakness is my impatience when it comes to people who are late for appointments or meetings. It frustrates me when I am punctual and other people are not. However, I am aware of this weakness and I am trying to understand that people have busy schedules and sometimes they can't always get to a meeting on time.

I need to be more understanding and have more patience when it comes to these kinds of situation. I think the weakness stems from me wanting to do a good job and I personally do not like wasting other people's time."

Q16. What attracts you to this post?

This is quite a common interview question during medical interviews and one that is relatively easy to answer. However, you need to make sure your answer stands out from the other candidate's responses. To begin with, get hold of the job description for the role and you will be able to structure a good response using this as a basis for your preparation.

Take a look at the following sample job description:

• Assess, plan, develop, implement and evaluate programmes to promote health and well-being, and prevent adverse effects on health and well-being.

• Implement and evaluate individual treatment plans for patients with a known long-term condition.

• Identify, and manage as appropriate, treatment plans for patients at risk of developing a long-term condition.

• Prioritise health problems and intervene appropriately to assist the patient in complex, urgent or emergency situations, including initiation of effective emergency care.

• Support patients to adopt health promotion strategies that encourage patients to live healthily, and apply principles of self-care.

Now take a look at the following response to the above question which is based around the key elements of the job description:

"One of my strengths is having the ability to assess, plan and develop programmes that are designed to promote health and wellbeing, so I believe I can bring a lot to the team in this respect. I am a very good organiser and therefore this role is attractive to me because you need

to be able to prioritise effectively in order to assist in patient care. I am also a very good communicator and the fact that the successful candidate will need to be able to encourage patients to lead healthy lives just makes it even more attractive to me".

Q17. What are the challenges that face this profession over the next 10 years?

This question has been designed to assess your knowledge and understanding of the medical profession. If you have an understanding of what is happening within the profession, then this demonstrates to the panel that you take an active interest in what's going on around you, and also on matters that will affect you directly.

Consider the following points when constructing your answer:

- Try reading medical profession journals and visit websites such as www.patient.co.uk and www.dh.gov.uk. In the lead up to your interview keep abreast of the more significant issues that affect your profession and have an opinion on each topical subject.

- Do not be negative about certain issues when responding to this question. Clearly one of the problems that affects the medical profession presently, and will continue to do so in the future, is that of 'burn out'. When talking about topical subjects like this, try to offer up a positive solution to the matter rather than talking negatively about how the issue is affecting you, your team and also the profession in general.

Now let's move on to situational interview questions and how to respond to them.

CHAPTER 5
SITUATIONAL INTERVIEW QUESTIONS

SITUATIONAL INTERVIEW QUESTIONS

Situational interview questions are designed to assess your experience in a particular area. In order to respond to these types of questions effectively, you will need to provide specific examples of where you have already gained experience in a similar situation. Let us first of all take a look at a sample situational interview question:

Q18. Describe a situation where you had to give negative feedback to someone.

You will note that the question is asking you to 'describe a situation'. Do not fall into the trap of responding in a manner that tells the panel what you 'would do' if this type of situation was to arise. Instead, explain what you 'did do' during a specific situation.

Structuring your responses to situational interview questions

A great way to structure responses to situational interview questions is by using the **STAR** method. Whilst we have already covered this in detail, let's recap:

S - Situation

T - Task

A - Action

R - Result

Here is a brief summary of each of the above areas:

Situation - start off by providing the interview panel with a brief explanation of the situation. Who was involved and what was the problem or situation?

Task - then go on to explain what had to be done. What was the task?

Action - now explain what action you took, and what action others took in order to achieve the task.

Result - finally explain what the result was from your actions. Try to make out that the end result was positive as a result of your input and influence.

Now take a look at the sample response to the above question. Remember to use the STAR method when constructing your responses to situation interview questions and you won't go far wrong!

Q18. Describe a situation where you had to give negative feedback to someone.

"I was working on a ward approximately 3 months ago, supervising a new team. Some members of the team were relatively new to the post so I made sure I provided a solid, in-depth brief at the commencement of the shift. As the shift progressed I noticed one of the nurses talking to a patient in an unacceptable manner. The patient was struggling to get out of bed and the nurse, instead of being patient and assisting carefully, was being overly forceful in her instructions.

Once the nurse had finished assisting the patient I called her to one side and asked whether she thought she could have handled the situation in a better manner. Unfortunately, she did not pick up on the fact that she had been rude to the patient, so I explained what I had witnessed and I explained how her actions were unacceptable. I explained our patient charter and the standard of care that our patients rightly deserve, and also what I would expect as a doctor.

Once I had explained in detail what was expected, she agreed that she could have handled the situation better. I then arranged for some further training for her in patient care, and since then she has become a better nurse, and a better member of our team as a result of this experience.

My aim throughout this situation was to try and improve the standard of care that our patients receive and I believe I achieved that in a constructive and educational manner."

Q19. Can you provide a situation where you have experienced conflict with a work colleague?

We have all experienced some form of conflict with work individuals at some point. The panel are looking to see how you deal with such conflict.

Consider the following points when responding to this type of interview question:

- It is essential that you remain calm throughout. Never become angry or confrontational.

- Assertiveness is acceptable, but do not cross the line from assertiveness to anger.

- Demonstrate effective communication skills, both listening and verbally. Try to listen to the other person's point of view or concerns.

- Try to demonstrate to the panel how you resolved the conflict in a positive manner.

- Always put the needs of the team first.

Q20. Give an example of a situation where your work was criticised.

Consider the following points when responding to a question of this nature:

- It is perfectly acceptable to say you made a mistake. It is what you do afterwards upon reflection that is important.

- Demonstrate an understanding of the error you made and also the reasons why you made the error. Tell the panel that you 'reflected' on your actions and sought for ways to improve.

- Finish off on a positive note by saying what you did to improve for next time.

Take a look at the following response:

"I can remember lifting a patient from their bed with a work colleague. Afterwards, I was heavily criticised by the Staff Nurse for using incorrect manual handling procedures.

I listened carefully to her feedback and I soon realised she was right, I had in fact used incorrect techniques which could have caused an injury. Upon reflection, I identified where I had gone wrong. The reason for my error was it was a very busy weekend evening on the ward and I was in a hurry to get the task complete. However, this is no excuse and I could have injured myself or even worse the patient. The following day I re-familiarised myself with manual handling procedures and since then I always ensure I carry out the correct procedures, regardless of the time constraints."

Q21. How would you cope with a situation if someone was being critical of your work?

Take a look at the following response to this question:

"Because I am passionate about my work, and I care about the job, I would naturally be disappointed. However, I would be keen to hear their feedback and I would listen carefully to their concerns.

If I agreed with their comments then I would certainly take immediate action to rectify the problem and improve or change my way of working. If I disagreed with them, then I would seek a second opinion before taking action. Just because someone is critical of your work doesn't necessarily mean they are right. It is sometimes good practice to get a second opinion. I am very good at taking criticism and I never take it personally.

The most important thing is the team that I work in and overall goals of the organisation. It is my responsibility to make sure I am at the top of my game. If that means taking on-board criticism then I am more than happy to listen and learn."

Q22. How would you handle a disagreement with another member of staff over the management of a patient's care?

This type of question can be quite tricky to answer. However, with a little fore-thought you can construct an excellent response.

Consider the following points whilst creating your response:

- Patient care is paramount.

- Disagreements between work colleagues can look unprofessional, so discuss matters in a private room whenever possible.

- A second opinion, if available, is sometimes the right option.

- Always try to get to the root of the problem. Why was there a disagreement and how can it be resolved so that it doesn't happen again?

Take a look at the following answer for some useful tips:

"The most important aspect in this type of situation is the care of the patient and therefore an agreement must be reached as soon as possible. If I were disagreeing with a colleague on the ward, and we were close to other patients, then I would suggest we went somewhere private to discuss and resolve the matter.

If it was too difficult and we could not reach an agreement then I would suggest a second opinion from a senior nurse or doctor. Once a decision had been made, then it would be time to sit down and sort out why there was such a disagreement in the first place, so that it didn't happen again.

In this type of situation I would always remain professional, calm and keep the interests of the patient at the forefront of my mind."

Q23. How do you resolve situations of conflict between work colleagues?

Consider the following points when responding to this type of question:

- The medical organisation's needs and the needs of the patient must always come first.

- There is no room for personal differences at work. You must put your differences aside and ensure that you have a professional relationship with all work colleagues, no matter how much you may dislike certain individuals.

- Sometimes you may need to be the 'better person' and go along with someone else's decision for the sake of a patient, even if you strongly disagree.

- Always try to resolve individual differences. Sometimes just by talking to the other person with a view to resolving an issue can get it sorted out swiftly and amicably.

Take a look at the following response:

"Regardless of the situation I would always remain calm and professional. The needs of the team, organisation and the patient must come first. Individual differences should be left outside of work, but I would always try to resolve a situation if I thought it was impacting on a work relationship. For example, last year I had a difference of opinion with a work colleague on a ward. I was keen for the situation not to escalate and so I invited them to meet me outside of work in a relaxed atmosphere for a coffee and a chat, with a view to sorting out the conflict. Just by meeting them outside of work we immediately settled our differences. I believe the fact that we were outside of the potentially stressful environment gave us both time to reflect on our thoughts and reach an amicable way forward. As a result of that meeting, we became closer work colleagues. I would try my hardest to listen to their views and opinions and take them on board wherever necessary.

I do not enjoy confrontation but if it appears, then I am not afraid to deal with it in a professional manner. As I mentioned at the beginning, the needs of the team, organisation and patient must always come first."

Q24. Can you provide an example of where you used effective communication skills that made a difference to a patient?

Communication skills are very important to your role. If you are a good communicator then your job will be much easier. Communication skills generally fall into two categories as follows:

- Listening communication skills
- Verbal communication skills.

Each one of the above is just as important as the other.

Consider the following points when responding to this question:

- It is good practice to gather facts and information about a situation before making a decision. Sometimes this will not be possible but in general, you should take the time to listen carefully, ask questions and gather relevant information before making decisions that affect others.

- Use effective listening skills, such as nodding to agree and also to demonstrate you are paying attention. Use facial expressions to demonstrate sympathy or empathy. You don't always have to say something to show that you are listening.

- When listening to a patient try to avoid distractions and focus on them and their specific needs.

- When talking to a patient, speak in a calm manner. Often a gentle, softer voice can work wonders on a patient who is concerned, anxious or worried. Use your initiative to gauge the type of communication skills you need for each given situation. For example, if communicating with a child you will need to use an altogether different approach.

- If a patient appears to be concerned or anxious then try talking about a subject that is totally separate from their condition. This will allow you to build up a rapport with then.

Now let's move on to a number of sample leadership style interview questions.

CHAPTER 6

LEADERSHIP, RESEARCH & ORGANISATIONAL INTERVIEW QUESTIONS

LEADERSHIP, RESEARCH & ORGANISATIONAL INTERVIEW QUESTIONS

Q25. Can you tell us about a situation where you demonstrated leadership?

Before we take a look at a sample response to this question, first we need to explore the definition of 'leadership'. A simple definition is that leadership is the art of motivating a group of people to act towards achieving a common goal. Put even simpler, the leader is the inspiration and director of the action. He or she is the person in the group that possesses the combination of personality and skills that makes others want to follow his or her direction.

Ok, now that we understand what leadership means, here is a sample response:

"One evening, at the change of shift, I became aware that two members of the nursing team were late for work. There had been heavy snowfall that day and the congestion on the surrounding roads meant that many people could not get to work. I took it upon myself to lead the team throughout the coming shift, and despite being two people down we managed to achieve the goal of providing first class treatment and care.

To begin with, I briefed the remainder of the team on the difficulty of the task that lay ahead of us. I assessed the skill levels and experience of each team member and allocated tasks accordingly. I ensured that I remained confident and in control during the brief so that the team members would have confidence in my ability to manage the problem.

As the shift progressed I had a number of different problems to deal with but I remained calm, listened carefully to the problems and directed accordingly. At the end of the shift we congratulated ourselves on a job well done and discussed the areas in which we felt we could improve on, if the same situation was to arise again."

Q26. Can you explain the difference between a manager and a leader?

Before constructing your response to this question, take a look at the following information:

Leadership is a facet of management and is therefore just one of the many assets a successful manager must possess. The main aim of a manager is to maximise the output of the organisation through administrative implementation. To achieve this, managers must undertake the following functions:

- organisation
- planning
- staffing
- directing
- controlling

Leadership is just one important component of the directing function. A manager cannot just be a leader; he or she also needs formal authority to be effective. In some circumstances, leadership is not required. For example, self-motivated groups may not require a single leader and may find leaders dominating. The fact that a leader is not always required proves that leadership is just an asset and is not essential.

In a nutshell, the difference between the two is as follows:

- Leadership is setting a new direction or vision for a group that they follow, i.e. a leader is the spearhead for that new direction.
- Management controls or directs people/resources in a group according to principles or values that have already been established.

If you can provide specific examples in your response where you have demonstrated leadership skills and also management skills, then even better!

Q27. What makes a good leader?

In order to become a good leader you must have a number of different skills that you can draw upon at a moment's notice. These include:

Visionary

Good leaders create a vision, a picture of the future, of where they want to take their organisations or team.

Inspirational

Once a vision is established, great leaders can inspire everyone in the team to get on board and start working towards the goal.

Strategic

Strategic leaders are clear and they directly face the strengths and weaknesses of their own teams. They effectively plan for the future.

Focused

Once the vision and mission are established, good leaders achieve what they set out to do before launching new initiatives.

Likeable

Good leaders are liked by the majority of people who work for them. They quickly recognise that interpersonal skills are paramount.

Decisive

Good leaders can make decisions quickly -- often with incomplete information. As Theodore Roosevelt said, "In any moment of decision, the best thing you can do is the right thing, the next best thing is the wrong thing, and the worst thing you can do is nothing."

Open to feedback

Good leaders are open and dedicated to lifelong learning.

Ethical

Good leaders are direct and straightforward. They set clear performance expectations and hold people accountable.

Q28. What can you tell us about the role that you've applied for?

The first step is to read the job description and person specification carefully.

Once you understand these and their content, you will be able to construct an excellent response.

In order to further improve your response I strongly recommend that you speak to people whom are already working within the team, trust or organisation. That way you will be able to provide a response which is more relevant to the actual role. If, when you are talking to nurses and medical staff within the team, it becomes apparent that they are complaining about certain problems within the team or management, do not repeat these back at interview.

Focus purely on the positive aspects of the role and some of the challenges that the team may face either now or in the future. It is important that you demonstrate to the interview panel that you have gone out of your way to find out about the role and the team that you would be working within.

Q29. Why is research important to your role?

As we're sure you'll agree research is crucial to your role within the medical profession. It is important that you keep abreast of procedural changes, regulations and other important information that affects your role.

When responding to this type of question you must formulate a response that demonstrates to the panel you appreciate the importance of research.

Take a look at the following sample response:

"Research is important to my role as a doctor because it allows me to perform to a consistently high standard. If a week goes by where I fail to keep abreast with the changes then this could potentially have a negative effect on my ability to perform.

I therefore ensure that I spend a set period of time each week keeping up-to-date with procedural changes and researching information about my role. I usually carry out my research at home when I am not at work as this allows me to concentrate solely on the information I am reading."

Once you have answered this question you may then get asked question 30.

Q30. What have been the most recent changes to your role?

This follow on question is designed to see whether or not you do actually carry out research as you say you do. Therefore, before you attend the interview, make sure you are fully aware of the most recent changes to your role.

Q31. What is Evidence Based Medicine?

Evidence-based medicine (EBM) aims to apply evidence gained from the scientific method to certain parts of medical practice. It seeks to assess the quality of evidence relevant to the risks and benefits of treatments (including lack of treatment). According to the Centre for Evidence-Based Medicine:

> *"Evidence-based medicine is the conscientious, explicit and judicious use of current best evidence in making decisions about the care of individual patients."*

EBM recognises that many aspects of medical care depend on individual factors such as quality and value-of-life judgments, which are only partially subject to scientific methods.

For more information about this subject please visit **www.cebm.net.**

Q32. What is your understanding of the term 'Research Governance'?

When responding to this type of question, try to include the following areas within the context of your answer:

An explanation of what it is

Research Governance is the broad range of regulations, principles and standards of good practice that exist to achieve, and continuously improve, research quality across all aspects of healthcare in the UK and throughout the entire world.

Who it applies to

Research Governance generally applies to everyone who is connected to healthcare research. By healthcare research, we mean any health-related research which involves humans, their tissue and/or data.

Examples of Research Governance

- Analysis of data from a patient's medical notes
- Observations
- Conducting surveys
- Using non-invasive imaging
- Using blood or other tissue samples
- Inclusion in trials of drugs, devices and surgical procedures

Why it is needed

- To safeguard participants in research.
- To protect researchers/investigators.
- To enhance ethical and scientific quality.
- To minimise risk.
- To monitor practice and performance.
- To promote good practice and ensure lessons are learned.

CHAPTER 7
TEACHING AND TRAINING
INTERVIEW QUESTIONS

TEACHING AND TRAINING INTERVIEW QUESTIONS

Q33. What teaching experience do you have so far?

Having the ability to teach, motivate, and inspire others are qualities that are essential to certain roles within the medical profession. There will be an expectation within certain roles to teach others; therefore, it is important that you can demonstrate a level of experience in this area.

If you can provide specific examples of where you have taught others, then this would be preferable. However, if you have little or no experience then there are still a number of options available to you when responding to this type of question:

1. Embark on some form of teacher training programme in your spare time.

This could be done through distance learning, a book or a DVD. Explain to the interview panel that you have researched the subject and explain to them what you know about it. Talk them through how you would teach, motivate and inspire your students.

2. Get a group of work colleagues together during a break or after a shift and give a presentation on a topical subject.

This will enable you to gain valuable experience in teaching and presenting and it will also give you a specific example to tell the interview panel.

Q34. Talk me through a presentation. How would you deliver your subject?

This type of question is only easy to respond to if you already have some experience in this area.

I have provided a free video on YouTube.com that will teach you how to give a presentation. Search for **'CareerVidz'** on YouTube and you will be able to find the video.

When responding to this question talk the panel through the following stages:

1. Pre-presentation preparation. (What you would do before the presentation, what research you would carry out and how you would prepare).

2. The presentation itself. (Explain how you would deliver the presentation).

3. Post presentation. (What would you do after the presentation?)

Now take a look at the following response to this type of question.

"To begin with, I would prepare fully for the presentation. This would involve setting a date for the presentation to take place, choosing a location, informing the students of the date, time and location, and making sure the correct facilities were available such as PowerPoint, projector, flip chart and other accessories. I would also ensure that there were suitable refreshments available for the students throughout the day.

Prior to the presentation I would carry out plenty of research into the subject matter and I would also carry out a practice run with a friend or work colleague so that my presentation skills were rehearsed and polished. The last thing I would want to do is deliver a poor presentation.

On the day of the presentation I would arrive early and get the room ready. Once everyone had arrived I would check they were sitting comfortably and then go through a few preliminaries such as fire alarm policy and fire escape, toilet facilities, asking questions, and anything else that was deemed appropriate at the time. Whilst delivering my presentation I would break it down into manageable portions and I would also ensure that I checked to see each student understood the subject matter. To make the subject matter easier to digest I would make the presentation interactive for the students by creating small group discussions and exercises. This would enable them to learn through interaction, which is far more effective than simply delivering a presentation by overhead projector and slides.

Once the lesson plan had been delivered I would seek confirmation of learning by summarising and also asking the students questions based around the information they had just received. At the end of the presentation I would provide the students with my contact details so that they could contact me to ask questions if they needed clarification at any time on a particular subject."

Q35. What is problem based learning?

Problem-based learning (PBL) is effectively a student-centred instructional strategy in which students collaboratively solve problems and reflect on their experiences. The main characteristics of PBL are:

- The learning is driven by challenging, open-ended problems.
- The students work in small collaborative groups to maximise learning.
- The teachers take on the role as the "facilitators" of learning.

Throughout PBL, students are encouraged to take responsibility for their group and organise and direct the learning process with support from a tutor or instructor. PBL can be used to enhance content knowledge and it can also foster the development of communication, problem-solving, and self-directed learning skills.

Q36. How would you identify your own training needs?

The first step in identifying your own training needs is to identify any gap between the skills your organisation needs, and those that you already have.

You will need to gather information and be honest about the areas where you could improve your performance. You could use surveys, observation, patient comments, and also organisational meetings to collect this information.

This training needs analysis will help you clarify your objectives in training and this will in turn help you improve the organisation or trust.

To carry out a training needs analysis on yourself, you need to:

- Establish the organisational goals and the skills required to meet these goals.
- What information or training you will need to be effective in your job.

- Establish what your preferred learning method would be.
- Establish what funding is available for your training.
- Take a decision on which type of training fits your needs best.

Q37. How do you keep your skills up-to-date?

Continuing Professional Development (CPD) is a continual learning pro-cess that complements formal undergraduate and postgraduate education and training. CPD requires doctors to maintain and improve their standards across all areas of their practice.

Keeping your skills up-to-date can be time consuming. Therefore, it is important that the time you allocate to this area is of value.

When responding to this question, consider the following key points:

1. Where do you go to keep up to date with Continual Professional Development (CPD)?

Consider journals, websites, discussion groups and training etc.

2. Individual doctors need to keep themselves up-to-date in all areas of Good Medical Practice.

These include:

- Good professional practice
- Maintaining good medical practice
- Relationships with patients
- Working with colleagues
- Teaching and training
- Probit
- Health

3. What you do in your CPD should be relevant to your practice, trust or organisation. You should, therefore:

a. Take into account the context and environment of your organisation; and:

b. Explore the benefits of learning across professional disciplines and boundaries.

CHAPTER 8

DIFFICULT WORK SITUATIONS INTERVIEW QUESTIONS

DIFFICULT WORK SITUATIONS INTERVIEW QUESTIONS

Q38. How would you deal with a colleague who was continually late for work?

Take a look at the following response to this question:

"Whether I was responsible managerially for the work colleague or not I would still take action. There are two issues here. The first issue is that the work colleague may need help or assistance in their personal or work life, and this may be the root cause as to why they are continually late. The second issue is that this type of problem can have a negative impact on the team and the wider organisation.

To begin with I would speak to the colleague in a quiet place away from any distractions, and at a time when there were no pressures of work. Depending on the situation, I may consider meeting them outside of working hours for a coffee or quiet drink; depending on how well I knew them. I would ask them if they had any problems outside of work that were impacting on their ability to make it into work on time. I would listen carefully to what they had to say before making any judgements or decisions. Once I had gathered all of the relevant facts, I would offer up a number of solutions to the problem. It maybe that they are finding it difficult to get to work on time due to external issues such as family problems, or it may be that they are finding it difficult to come to work due to an internal issue.

Either way I would offer my support and work with them to come up with a solution to the problem. If, at any time during our conversation I felt that the situation was out of my control or influence, then I would look to involve either a supervisory manager or other relevant person."

Q39. A patient mentions to you that they have smelt alcohol on the breath of a nurse on two separate occasions over the last two weeks. What do you do?

Take a look at the following response to this question:

"Before making any decisions it is essential to gather the facts. The priority here is patient safety, both immediate and long-term. I have a duty to act quickly in order to protect the patient, and that is what I would essentially do. Good medical practice also dictates that I should be willing to deal openly and supportively with problems in the performance, conduct or health of team members. I would share my concerns with an appropriate senior person such as the clinical director, making sure I adhered to trust procedures and guidelines.

At all times, I would offer my support to the nurse and I would be aware that he/she may have personal problems that need addressing. The level of support I offer and the assistance I provide would very much depend on the nature of the problem and also how well I knew the person. It may be that the team would need to be flexible if the nurse needed time away from clinical duties in order to rectify the problem. At all times I would be supportive; however, patient care is absolutely paramount."

Q40. If you witnessed a patient verbally abusing a nurse, what would you do?

Situations of this nature must be dealt with immediately in line with trust practice and guidance. Whilst the safety and care of the patient is important this does not mean to say that any member of staff should tolerate or accept any form of abuse, either physically or verbally.

Depending on the guidelines that are relevant to your trust or establishment, you may need to call security. Alternatively, depending on the nature and severity of the incident, you may be able to deal with it by informing the patient that any further abuse will be dealt with by the Police. Either way, it is important that the abuse stops immediately.

Q41. One of your consultants is managing a patient outside of the recommended guidance provided in NICE. What is NICE and how would

you handle this type of situation?

NICE stands for National Institute for Health and Clinical Excellence. NICE was established in 1999 and its main role is to make recommendations on treatment and care. Part of the role of NICE is to provide recommendations based on cost-effectiveness so you will not always get the best advice.

In essence NICE provides 4 different types of evidence:

1. Public Health Guidance.

2. Clinical Guidance.

3. Technology Appraisals.

4. Interventional Procedures Advice.

You can find out more information about NICE here:

www.nice.org.uk

When dealing with the situation above you need to first of all establish the facts and consider the following points:

- Because NICE offers recommendations based on cost-effectiveness, the consultant may not have thought the guidelines were appropriate for this type of situation.

- The guidance provided by NICE may not be applicable to the patient and therefore you will need to confirm this first.

- Check to see if the guidance is still relevant and in date.

- There is a slight possibility that the patient refuses to go along with the guidance offered and as a result they opted for an alternative option.

You will see from the above information provided that you will need to establish the correct facts before making a decision.

Q42. What would you do if a female junior colleague refused to treat a patient who was a known rapist?

Take a look at the following sample response to this question:

"This is a very difficult situation to deal with but one that must be dealt with in accordance with procedures and guidelines. All patients are entitled to care and treatment to meet their clinical needs. A work colleague must not refuse to treat a patient because they are a known rapist. If the junior colleague felt that the patient posed a risk to her health or safety, then I would take all available steps to minimise the risk for her, including the presence of another member of staff.

It would be important that I spoke to her about her feelings initially to gauge the exact reasons why. There may be more to the situation than is first apparent, so I would need to gather information and facts before deciding on the best course of action.

The patients care is a priority and I would ensure that this came first regardless of the circumstances. I would ensure that the patient was not discriminated against in any manner."

Q43. What would you do if a junior work colleague refused to treat a patient because of his background?

The investigations or treatment you provide or arrange must be based on the assessment you and the patient make of their needs and priorities, and on your clinical judgement about the likely effectiveness of the treatment options.

You must not refuse or delay treatment because you believe that a patient's actions have contributed to their condition. You must treat your patients with respect whatever their life choices and beliefs. You must not unfairly discriminate against them by allowing your personal views* to affect adversely your professional relationship with them or the treatment you provide or arrange. You should challenge colleagues if their behaviour does not comply with this guidance.

*This includes your views about a patient's age, colour, culture, disability, ethnic or national origin, gender, lifestyle, marital or parental status, race, religion or beliefs, sex, sexual orientation, or social or economic status.

Q44. A patient arrives at the hospital with gunshot wounds. Do you need to inform the Police?

Yes, you do, because gunshot wounds are the result of a serious incident. The police should always be told whenever a person has arrived at a hospital with a gunshot wound. However, it is not usually your responsibility to inform the Police of his or her personal details. It will normally be the responsibility of the Police to gather facts, information and evidence.

Q45. You have informed the Police that one of your patients has gunshot wounds. When they arrive they demand to see the patient immediately. The patient is currently being treated. What do you do?

The treatment and care of the patient is your first concern. You should not allow the Police access to the patient if this will delay or hamper treatment or even compromise the patient's recovery.

If patients' treatment and condition allow them to speak to the police, a member of the health care team should ask patients whether they are willing to do so, and if not explain what the consequences, if any, may be. The health care team and the police must abide by the patient's decision.

Q46. Whilst carrying out pre natal checks on a healthy pregnant woman, she informs you that she wants a free birth. What is a free birth and is it permitted?

A free birth (sometimes referred to as free birthing) means a woman gives birth without medical or professional help. ('Free birthing' should not be confused with 'natural childbirth' or with a birth attended by a self-employed, often known as an independent midwife). This practice is legal providing the birth is not undertaken by an 'unqualified individual'. An 'unqualified individual' is someone who is not a registered doctor or midwife but attempts to take up that role during birth.

The woman assumes full responsibility for her child's birth, but she may and can have her partner, a relative or a friend present in a supportive role. If a woman chooses not to contact or engage a midwife, it is her absolute right to do so.

During your response to this question you would strongly advise the woman that she discusses the pros and cons of 'free birthing' with a suitably qualified person and gives serious consideration to any identified risks that may be associated with 'free birthing' and their personal, individual circumstances.

CHAPTER 9

CLINICAL GOVERNANCE INTERVIEW QUESTIONS

CLINICAL GOVERNANCE INTERVIEW QUESTIONS

Q47. What is Clinical Governance?

"Clinical governance is the system through which NHS organisations are accountable for continuously improving the quality of their services and safeguarding high standards of care, by creating an environment in which clinical excellence will flourish."

Q48. Can you explain how Clinical Governance affects patient care and safety?

Take a look at the following sample response to this question:

"Clinical Governance should, in theory, have a positive effect on a patient's safety. However, if clinical governance is to truly function effectively as a systematic approach to maintaining and improving the quality of patient care and safety, within a health system, it requires advocates. It also requires systems and people to be in place to promote and develop it.

There are essentially three key aspects within Clinical Governance that will impact on patient care and safety. These are establishing recognisably high standards of care, transparent responsibility and accountability for those standards, and also a constant dynamic of improvement.

If these three elements are in place then Clinical Governance will continue to have a positive impact on patient care and safety."

Q49. How does Clinical Governance impact on your day-to-day work?

Only you will know exactly how Clinical Governance impacts on your daily work. However, before responding to this type of question bear in mind the following:

Clinical Governance is a systematic approach to maintaining and improving the quality of patient care. Therefore, it has to have some benefit within your organisation or trust. When constructing your response don't be negative. If you strongly believe that there is an issue with Clinical Governance then try to offer up a solution as to how it can be improved. Remember that you are being interviewed for a position that requires you to abide by rules and procedures, so answer the question responsibly and carefully.

Try to think of the positive aspects of Clinical Governance and put them across in your response.

Q50. What is a 'Near Miss'?

"A near miss can be defined as an occurrence, which but for luck or skilful management, would in all probability have become an incident."

Q51. What is Clinical Risk Management?

Clinical risk management aims to achieve the following four objectives:

1. Identification of organisational, system failures or defence inadequacies. This is so that managers can act to remedy the situation before an accident occurs.

2. The prompt collection of all relevant records as soon as possible after an accident.

3. Provide early warning of possible claims. Incident reporting allows up-to date information to be used to decide whether an organisation, should consider fighting or settling any clinical complaint.

4. Early incident reporting and analysis enables lessons to be learnt. This is through an objective assessment of all the active and latent human failures surrounding a particular event."

CHAPTER 10

MEDICAL SCHOOL
INTERVIEW QUESTIONS

MEDICAL SCHOOL INTERVIEW QUESTIONS

Q52. Why do you want to study medicine?

When preparing your response to this question you need to consider the following key areas:

1. Your desire to study medicine must be unique and personal. Every student will have their own reasons why they wanted to study medicine, and you should be no different.

2. Demonstrate a life-long passion for medicine when creating your response. If you have wanted to choose this career path for a long time, explain what ignited the passion in the first place and what drove it on subsequently.

3. Consider talking about your key qualities and attributes within your response. These should ideally match the requirements of the job you eventually want to end up doing. Some examples of positive qualities and attributes to offer the panel include compassion, dedication, flexibility, caring nature, resilience, determination, humour, knowledge and teamwork.

4. If you have any prior work experience within the medical profession use this during your response. Explain what you learnt during the experience and how it enhanced your passion to study medicine. Also provide specific examples of the type of work you undertook and what you most enjoyed about it.

5. If you, your friends or relatives have experience of being in medical care then it is perfectly acceptable to refer to their experiences during your response.

6. Refer to your personal statement during your response to this interview question if you feel the need to.

Now take a look at the following sample response to this question.

"I have wanted to work within the medical profession since I can re-member. Whilst at school my fondest memories were whilst studying science-based lessons. I simply found them intriguing and have always had a passion for the medical profession, hence the reason why I did so well during my education. During my teenage years I had a short spell in hospital and I can remember back then that this was the career for me. Since then I have worked hard to be in the position I am today

where I am applying for medical school.

During my stay in hospital the doctors and nurses were simply out-standing. The amount of effort they put into their work was inspirational. During my stay in hospital I learnt that patient care is at the forefront of every doctor and nurse. The manner in which they treated every patient on the ward was amazing.

Since those early years I have been focusing on developing the right qualities that would enable me to go to medical school. These qualities include an ability to communicate effectively with everyone, regardless of their background, an ability to work effectively as a team member, resilience, confidence, an ability to work unsupervised and also an ability to continually improve myself. I believe through my experiences and education so far, I would make the ideal candidate for medical school."

Q53. Tell me about yourself and why you think you will be successful in medical school?

When preparing a response to this question you need to concentrate on two elements:

1. Providing details about yourself that put you across in a positive manner;

2. Providing details of why you will be successful at medical school.

Here's a sample response to this question to assist you.

"My name is Richard, I am 25 years old and I currently reside in Kent. I am in my final year at Canterbury College studying A-levels for chemistry, biology, physics and maths. When not studying I enjoy working on my physical fitness and I spend time in my local gym and also playing for a local football team. I find that my good levels of physical fitness help me to concentrate during my studies for A-levels. With regards to my character, I would say that I am hard-working, confident, determined

and generous. I would also say that I am a caring person and more recently I spent 4 weeks of the summer holidays working as a volunteer at a local Demelza House charity shop in Canterbury. I undertook this work experience because I wanted to develop my personal and social skills in preparation for eventually getting a career in the medical profession.

I believe I would be successful at medical school simply because I have a track record for achieving and also a long-term passion for the medical profession which stems back many, many years. I am confident that I will achieve high grades on my A-levels because of the amount of work I have been putting into my studies. I do not drink alcohol and I find that this ensures my concentration levels are at their best at all times, something which I will need if I am going to be successful in achieving my dream of getting into medical school. Although I am very much capable of concentrating on my own individual studies and development, I believe I would be able to help the other students at medical school work towards achieving good grades. I believe that studying with other people during revision sessions is a great way to learn and improve, and this method of learning is something that I have used to great effect during my time at Canterbury College with the other students.

Finally, I would like to say that if I am given the opportunity to obtain a place at medical school it will not go to waste. I would grab the opportunity with both hands and ensure that I put in 100% effort to all of my studying and development."

Q54. If you are successful at medical school and go on to become a doctor, how would you like your work colleagues to perceive you?

This question is designed to assess what your priorities are and also what type of doctor you want to become. Everyone wants to be popular amongst their work colleagues, but it is important you strike a balance between popularity and professionalism. Before constructing your own response to this question, consider the following points:

- Your main priority as a doctor will be patient care.

- Doctors should act as role models for the medical organisation they are working for.

- As a doctor you must set an example to your work colleagues.

- Whilst it is important to be humorous when the situation permits, you should also act with professionalism and a high degree of integrity at all times.

Now take a look at the following sample response to this question which will be useful during your preparation.

"I would like them to perceive me as professional, conscientious, disciplined, organised individual and someone who is dedicated to delivering outstanding patient care. Whilst it is nice to be liked and accepted by your peers and work colleagues, I also believe it is more important to focus on working hard to meet the expectations of the medical profession or trust you are employed by. In essence, doctors should be positive role models to those who they work alongside. I also want to be seen as someone who is calm under pressure, knowledgeable and resilient in pressurised and difficult situations. I would like to be perceived as approachable; someone who people can come to if they need help or advice. Finally, I would want to ensure I maintained a sense of humour during work as I believe this will contribute towards a healthy environment for both work colleagues and patients."

Q55. What have you been doing to prepare for medical school?

Your preparation for medical school should start well in advance of the interview. It is important to be able to demonstrate to the interview panel that you have been working towards your goal for some time. This can be demonstrated in a number of different ways, as follows:

- Spending time with other people within the medical profession, such as doctors, nurses, general medical staff and ambulance workers. When speaking to them, find out about their daily workloads and also find out what a typical working day involves. Finding out about the different professions within the medical profession will give you an all-round view of the type of work that goes on. Don't just speak to doctors!

- Spend time speaking to current medical students who are on the course you are trying to enrol on. This will give you a greater understanding of what is involved and also what to expect from the course.

– Spending time reading appropriate medical journals and researching websites such as:

www.patient.co.uk

www.nhs.uk

www.nhsdirect.nhs.uk

www.doctors.net.uk

www.bmj.com

www.newscientist.com

http://bma.org.uk

NOTE: if you state during your interview that you read or visit any of these websites, makes sure you are familiar with their content. The interviewer may ask you to give an example of the latest content to be added to the website.

Take a look at the following sample response to this question which will help you to prepare.

"I started preparing for medical school before I commenced my A-levels as I knew this is where I wanted to eventually end up. I started off by reading and familiarising myself with the British Medical Journal to get an insight into the profession and also to keep abreast of changes and developments. Only yesterday I was reading up on the China SimSmoke tobacco policy model and was astounded to learn that currently over 50% of men in China still smoke. The policy aims to use a computer simulation model to project the potential impact in China of tobacco control measures on smoking. I understand it has been recommended by the World Health Organisation Framework Convention on Tobacco Control.

In addition to trying to keep abreast of what's happening within the medical profession, I have spent time speaking to people who work within the medical profession and also students who are enrolled on the current medical school course. I was fortunate enough to speak to doctors, nurses and general medical staff at Maidstone Hospital last month and found out what a typical working day involves for each of the different roles. I believe this provided me with an invaluable insight into the type of duties I would perform once I eventually become a qualified doctor. I felt it was also important to find out about the different roles within a doctors team, as I would essentially be working alongside them.

As mentioned, I also spent time with current medical students and this was a great experience. One student in particular showed me their timetable so I was able to gauge the amount of study time I would get each day. This is important for me to know as I like to plan well ahead with regards to study and revision. Overall, I have been preparing myself for quite a long time now as I am very passionate about the medical profession and have my heart set on getting a place in medical school."

Q56. How do you know you will be able to undertake the level of study required to become a doctor?

If you have a track record of studying for prolonged periods of time then this question should be relatively easy to answer. It is important when creating your response that you provide an example of where you have already revised and studied for long periods of time and, as a result, achieved success. Here is a sample response to this question to help you.

"Whilst I am not an arrogant person, I am 100% certain that I will be able to undertake the level of study required. To begin with, I believe I have already demonstrated during my previous studies that I have the

capability to study and take on-board lots of relevant information over a prolonged period time. As an example, I achieved very high grades in all of my GCSE's and I am confident I will achieve the same outcome with my A-level results.

Whilst I do enjoy socialising, I do not touch alcohol as a rule, and as a result, my energy and concentration levels are always high. I also believe that because I have a passion for the medical profession the studying will be enjoyable. Having said that, I am certainly not complacent and I understand that I will find certain elements of the course extremely tough and demanding.

In life, whenever I come up against difficult situations and obstacles I always work hard to overcome them. I will apply this same methodology and mind-set whilst studying at medical school."

Q57. So, you want to become a doctor? Tell us what the role involves?

If you have spent any time working alongside doctors, through voluntary work or otherwise, this question will be easy to answer. Whilst you can find information regarding a doctor's role online, nothing beats actually speaking to doctors face-to-face to find out what their entails. If you do get the chance to speak to working doctors, make sure you find out the following information:

- What a typical day involves, including the different types of challenges they will be faced with.

- The pros and cons of the job.

- How they deal with highly pressurised situations.

- The qualities they have which help them to deliver outstanding patient care.

To help you prepare for this question, here is some useful information relating to the role of a doctor.

Doctors alone amongst healthcare professionals must be capable of regularly taking ultimate responsibility for difficult decisions in situations of clinical complexity and uncertainty, drawing on their scientific knowledge and well-developed clinical judgement.

The doctor's role must be defined by what is in the best interest of patients and of the population served. Doctors as clinical scientists apply the principles and procedures of medicine to prevent, diagnose, care for and treat patients with illness, disease and injury and to maintain physical and mental health. They supervise the implementation of care and treatment plans by others in the health care team and conduct medical education and research. All healthcare professionals require a set of generic attributes to merit the trust of patients that underpins the therapeutic relationship. These qualities include good communication skills, the ability to work as part of a team, non-judgemental behaviour, empathy and integrity.

In addition to possessing these shared attributes doctors must be able to:

- assess patients' healthcare needs taking into account their personal and social circumstances.

- apply their knowledge and skills to synthesise information from a variety of sources in order to reach the best available diagnosis and understanding of the patient's problem, or to know what steps need to be taken to secure such an outcome.

- support patients in understanding their condition and what they might expect, including in those circumstances when patients present with symptoms that could have several causes.

- identify and advise on appropriate treatment options or preventive measures.

- explain and discuss the risks, benefits and uncertainties of various tests and treatments and where possible support patients to make decisions about their own care.

Q58. What training will you undergo during medical school?

Believe it or not, most students who apply to medical school will be unaware of the exact training they will undergo whilst at medical school. Make sure you are totally familiar with the training course, its content and duration. To help you prepare, here is a sample response to this question.

*"**Phase 1** of the course runs from September through to June and it covers the following subjects:*

- *Introductory Clinical Competency*
- *Introduction to Medical Studies and Medical Sciences*
- *Introductory clinical competencies*
- *Systems based learning and teaching*
- *Integrated Clinical Demonstrations*
- *Intensive Clinical Experience*
- *Research Project*
- *Medicine Society*
- *Student Selected Components*

The structure of Phase 1 follows the General Medical Council's (GMC) Guidelines and is largely 'systems-based'. Formal assessment in Phase 1 consists of a written examination paper (multiple-choice and clinically related 'scenario' questions) and a practical examination. The whole examination must be passed before I can progress to the next stage.

***Phase 2** then runs from June through to December and covers areas such as:*

- *Basic Clinical Competencies*
- *Clinical Attachments*
- *Medical Sciences*
- *Clinical Skills*

I understand that during Phase 2 I will spend most of my time in hos-

pital wards, operating theatres and outpatient clinics, learning the skills that I will need to join the medical profession. Phase 3 is two years in duration and runs from January through to the following December. It consist of areas such as:

- *Extended Clinical Competencies*
- *Clinical Team Attachments*
- *Child Health*
- *Women's Health*
- *Mental Health*
- *SSCs*
- *Medical Sciences*
- *Acute Clinical Care*
- *Continuing Clinical Care*
- *Community Health*
- *Specialty Clinical Attachments*
- *Further SSCs including Medical Audit*

Phase 3 *is predominantly clinical based and has an emphasis on 'hands-on' medicine. Finally, Phase 4 runs from January to June and covers:*

- *Advanced Clinical Competencies*
- *Final Preparation for becoming a Junior Doctor*
- *A four week SSC period*
- *Clinical Team Attachments*
- *F1 Shadowing*

From January till June of the final year, I understand that I will be immersed in clinical medicine."

Q59. Can you tell us about any relevant work experience you have carried out so far?

If you have carried out any work experience within the medical profession prior to applying for medical school, this will further demonstrate to the interview panel not only your desire and passion to work within this field, but that your dedication and passion are far greater than the average medical school applicant. In fact, most medical schools require you to have some relevant work experience; because it's so competitive this is now almost compulsory. Without it, you will significantly reduce your chances. Work experience should ideally be in a health-related field or any 'caring' environment.

Work experience in hospitals

It is not easy to secure work experience in a hospital, shadowing doctors, due to concerns about patient confidentiality, however you should try. Try writing to your local hospitals (there is often a work experience manager) as well as your local GP; you have nothing to lose by trying. Most hospitals offer work experience placements to 16-18 year olds. These include (but are not limited to):

- Barts Health which includes Barts, The London, Newham and Whipps Cross Hospitals,
- Imperial College Health Care which includes St Marys, Hammersmith and Charing Cross Hospitals,
- Guys & Thomas' Hospitals,
- Kings College Hospital,
- Chelsea & Westminister Hospital,
- Great Ormond Street Hospital for Children,
- Lewisham Hospital,
- St Georges Healthcare,
- Royal National Orthopaedic Hospital NHS Trust,
- Croydon University Hospital,
- Kingston Hospital,
- Ashford & St Peters Hospitals,
- Epsom and St Heliers Hospitals,
- Royal Surrey Hospital,

- Buckinghamshire Health Care,
- Hampshire Hospitals,
- Royal Berkshire Trust,
- Mid Essex Hospital Services,
- West Middlesex University Hospital,
- Maidstone & Tunbridge Wells Hospital, Kent,
- Heatherwood and Wexham Park Hospitals,
- Oxford University Hospitals,
- Cambridge University Hospitals,
- Kettering General Hospital,
- University Hospitals Bristol,
- North Bristol NHS Trust,
- Royal United Hospitals, Bath,
- Weston Area Health which includes Weston General Hospital,
- Dartford & Gravesham Trust, (Darent Valley Hospital),
- Bedford Hospital,
- Luton & Dunstable University Hospital,
- Norfolk & Norwich University Hospitals,
- United Lincolnshire Hospitals,
- University Hospitals Leicester,
- University Hospitals Birmingham,
- Heart of England Trust,
- Bradford Teaching Hospitals,
- Worcestershire Acute Hospitals,
- University Hospital Coventry & Warwickshire,
- University Hospital of North Staffordshire,
- The Shrewsbury & Telford Hospital,
- Derby Hospitals,

- The Newcastle Upon Tyne Hospitals,
- Gateshead Health (Queen Elizabeth Hospital, Dunston Hill Day Hospital and Bensham Hospital),
- City Hospitals Sunderland,
- Royal Liverpool and Broadgreen University Hospitals,
- York Teaching Hospital,
- Calderdale and Hudderfield,
- Lancashire Teaching Hospitals,
- Sheffield Teaching Hospitals,
- The Rotherham Trust,
- Nottingham University Hospitals,
- The Leeds Teaching Hospitals,
- University Hospital of South Manchester,
- The Penine Acute Hospitals,
- Stockport NHS Trust,
- The Dudley Group,
- NHS Lothian,
- Belfast Health and Social Care Trust,
- Musgrove Park Hospital (part of Taunton & Somerset Trust),
- University Hospital, Southampton,
- Portsmouth Hospitals,
- Brighton & Sussex Hospitals,
- South Devon Healthcare,
- Royal Cornwall Hospitals,
- Yeovil District Hospital,
- Plymouth Hospitals.

Most, if not all hospitals have a team of volunteers to help both staff and patients. Volunteers' help with refreshments, show people where to go, keep patients company and provide practical support for the staff. Through this type of work, you can learn about how hospitals run and see what happens on medical wards. You can also spend lots of time with patients in a caring or supportive role, which is ideal for anyone applying to medical school.

Other ways to gain work experience

Hospice Volunteering

Hospices provide care for patients who are terminally ill. Many hospices rely heavily on volunteers to help with their work. This might involve helping with meal times, patient transport or day trips.

Health Care Assistant

There are also several paid jobs that you can do that don't require much prior training or experience. For example, you can work as a health care assistant (HCA), support worker, phlebotomist or hospital porter, all of which will give you excellent experience working with patients. Getting this type of job is particularly useful if you are taking a gap year or if you are going into medicine as a mature student. You can also work part time in many of these jobs. To get this type of work, look in the local paper, contact your local hospital, look for local nursing agencies or try the NHS jobs site.

Caring For Elderly

Caring for the elderly is also excellent experience for would-be doctors. This can often be challenging, as you may need to deal with patients with dementia, hearing loss and physical disability. The best way to search for this type of voluntary work is to look for your local nursing home or rest home and write to them, explaining why you would like to volunteer. Try the yellow pages website as a starting point

Counselling

There are lots of opportunities to work with organisations providing telephone counselling and support. Examples include Childline, who help children in distress, The Samaritans who offer support to adults in crisis and Saneline, who offer advice and counselling to people affected by mental illness.

Q60. During your work experience, what skills did you learn?

This question is aimed at determining whether or not you paid attention during your work experience placement and actually got something valuable from it. During work experience keep a daily diary of the type of situations you became involved in, the tasks you undertook, any shadowing you became involved in and also the experiences and qualities you gained. You should also try to obtain a letter from the work experience manager at the end of your work experience detailing the types of tasks you undertook/shadowed. This letter can then be passed on to the interview panel to provide actual evidence of your time there.

To assist you, here is a sample response to the question.

"I was fortunate enough to be offered a work experience placement at the Royal Surrey Hospital. The experience was fantastic and I became involved in tasks such as welcoming patients and visitors to the Hospital, accompanying patients and visitors to the clinics and wards, helping with 'trolley round' and also being part of the library service. I also managed to spend a day working with the Hospital radio station and was given the chance to do a 15 minute slot live on air talking about my passion for becoming a doctor.

During my time at the hospital I witnessed some amazing feats of work by the doctors, nurses and general medical staff. For example, I volunteered to work an extra evening shift at the weekends and the level of teamwork during the hospitals busiest times was amazing. I managed to get some time talking to patients on a few of the different wards to see how they were finding the experience of being in hospital and what they felt about the NHS staff. This was particularly useful to see and hear how the patients felt about the level of care they were receiving.

Above all, I learnt that teamwork and communication are vital to all roles within the hospital. Without these qualities the hospital would not be able to deliver the level of service it does day in, day out. I was not surprised to learn that the hospital had previously won the Enhancing Quality Award for best Performing Trust in the Region."

Q61. You mentioned that you took up a work placement at a local hospital. If you were in charge of the hospital, what would you change and why?

This is a very difficult question to answer and one that should be answered with care. I recommend that whilst carrying out your work experience placement you talk to the members of staff, doctors and staff and ask them what they would like to see changed at the hospital. If there is a common answer amongst the staff, you might be able to use this during your response. Take a look at the following tactful response which you may be able to use as a guide for creating your own.

"During my time at the hospital I did ask questions of the staff to see what the most difficult and frustrating elements of the job were. On the surface, everything appeared fine, but there was a common answer amongst staff, which was they felt they did not get enough quality time, speaking to the patients. To me, everything appeared fine as I felt that all members of staff were doing a tremendous job on the ground. However, upon reflection, I could see why they had concerns about the lack of available time they had to speak to the patients. Understandably, most of the patients would spend hours each day on their own and this must be quite frustrating for them, especially when waiting for visiting hours to start. Having said all of that, overall I felt that the hospital was run extremely efficiently given the level of resources available to the doctors and senior management team."

Q62. What qualities do you think a competent doctor should have?

Undoubtedly you will have learnt a tremendous amount so far about the role of a doctor and this question will be your opportunity to demonstrate the qualities and attributes required to perform the role competently. If you understand what the qualities and attributes of a competent doctor are prior to enrolling at medical school, then you will have a better chance of becoming one yourself once you graduate. Take a look at the following sample response to this question which will aid you during your preparation.

"Competent doctors require a large number of skills and attributes. To begin with, they need enthusiasm, passion and a high level of energy to carry out their work. Being a doctor can be demanding both physically and mentally, and he or she will need to have a level of drive that ensures they can perform to the best of their ability day in, day out.

Doctors also need to be highly knowledgeable; not only so they can deliver the most appropriate level of patient care, but so they can also advise junior members of staff on the best course of action for specific situations. They must also have the ability to remain calm in pressurised situations and adapt to an ever-changing environment. Flexibility is also another quality that is required, as is resilience and confidence. I also feel that doctors must be physically and mentally fit as the demands of the job can take their toll on the mind and body. By maintaining a good level of fitness, a doctor will be able to have a lengthy and rewarding career whilst delivering the high levels of patient care required by the trust he or she are working for. At times, doctors must also be humorous and be able to work effectively as part of the wider team environment.

Doctors must also be competent leaders and act as role models at all times, demonstrating good practice and a high level of professionalism. There are many other qualities and attributes that a doctor must possess, but these are the main ones that I feel will all go together to make a competent doctor."

Q63. Where do you see yourself in 5 years' time?

This question should be answered positively and with a degree of ambition. However, the degree of ambition should take into consideration the fact that you are yet to secure a place at medical school! Take a look at the following response, which will give you a good indication as to how to approach this type of question.

"I am certainly an ambitious person and within 5 years' time I want to be a qualified doctor who is achieving excellent results for the medical organisation I am working for by delivering outstanding patient care. Although I am highly ambitious, the most important thing for me in the short-term would be to pass medical school with excellent grades, learn my job properly and become competent in the role. It is also important for me to gain the respect of the other members of my team. In terms of future development, I would aim to have an ongoing programme of continuous professional development in place to ensure my skills as a doctor are improving all of the time. I want to be extremely good at my job and I want my employer to think that they have made the right choice in taking me on."

Q64. Can you tell me about any achievements you have experienced during your life so far?

Those people who can demonstrate a history of achievement are far more likely to secure a place at medical school. Having achieved something in your life demonstrates that you have the ability to see things through to the end, something that is crucial to your studies and professional development. It also shows that you are motivated and determined to succeed. Try to think of examples where you have succeeded or achieved something relevant in your life. Some good examples of achievements are as follows:

- Winning a trophy with a football or hockey team;

- Achieving high grades in your GCSEs, A-levels and other educational qualifications;

- Duke of Edinburgh's Award;

- Being given responsibility at school, college, university or at work;

- Raising money for charities and good causes.

Here is a sample response to assist you.

"Yes I can. So far in my life I have achieved quite a few things that I am proud of. To begin with I achieved good grades whilst at school including a grade 'A' in physics, chemistry and maths. I worked very hard to achieve my grades and I am proud of them.

At weekends I play rugby for a local team and I've achieved a number of things with them. Apart from winning the league last year we also held a charity match against the local Police rugby team. We managed to raise £500 for a local charity, which was a great achievement. More recently I managed to achieve a huge improvement in my fitness levels.

I have learnt that you have to work hard in life if you want to achieve things and I have a positive attitude to hard work. My own personal motto is 'work hard and you will be rewarded'. I genuinely believe that I have the determination, tenacity and intelligence to be successful at medical school."

Q65. What do you think the qualities of a good team player are?

Having knowledge of how a team operates and the qualities required to become a competent team player would be an advantage before you attend medical school. As we learnt during question 61, team work is just one of the qualities required to become a competent doctor. Take a look at the following 'team' qualities:

- An ability to interact and work with others, regardless of their age, sex, religion, sexual orientation, background, disability or appearance;

- Being able to communicate with everyone in the team and provide an appropriate level of support and encouragement;

- Being capable of carrying out tasks correctly, professionally and in accordance with organisational guidelines and regulations;

- Being focused on the team's goal(s);

- Having a flexible attitude and approach to the task;

- Putting the needs of the team or organisation first, before your own;

- Putting personal differences aside for the sake of the wider team;

- Being able to listen to others' suggestions and contributions.

When responding to this type of question it would be an advantage if you could back up your response with an example of where you have already worked in a team. Take a look at the following sample response:

"A good team player must have many different qualities including an ability to listen carefully to a given brief. If you don't listen to the brief that is provided then you can't complete the task properly. In addition to listening carefully to the brief you must be able to communicate effectively with everyone in the team. This will include providing support for the other team members and also listening to other people's suggestions on how a task can be achieved. You also have to be able to work with anyone in the team regardless of their age, background, religion, sexual orientation, disability or appearance. You can't discriminate against anyone and if you do, then there is no place for you within that team. As a doctor I understand that I will be working with people from all walks of life, and this is one of the most appealing aspects of the job.

A good team player must also be able to carry out his or her job professionally and competently. When I say competently, I mean correctly and in accordance with guidelines and the level of training that has been provided. You should also be focused on the team's or organisations goals and not be distracted by any external factors. Putting the needs of the team first is paramount. Finally, a good team player must be flexible and be able to adapt to the changing requirements of the team.

I already have some experience of working in a team and I know how important it is to work hard at achieving the task. In a previous job we would have a weekly team briefing. During the team briefings my manager would inform us what jobs need to be carried out as a priori-

ty. During one particular meeting he asked three of us to clear a fire escape that had become blocked with cardboard boxes, debris and rubbish. He also asked us to come up with a plan to prevent it from happening again. We quickly set about the task carefully removing the rubbish and I had the responsibility of arranging for a refuse collection company to come and dispose of the rubbish. We also had to work together to find ways of preventing the rubbish from being haphazardly disposed in the same way again in the future. We sat down together and wrote out a memorandum for our manager that he could distribute to all staff. At the end of the job we'd worked well to achieve the task and no more rubbish was ever disposed in the fire escape again. My manager was very pleased with the job we'd done."

Q66. Who do you think are the most important members of a doctor's team?

Most people would be forgiven for thinking that nurses are the most important members of a doctor's team. Whilst they are vital to the overall functioning of a ward, and for the delivery outstanding patient care, they are no more important than the rest of the team. If one element of a medical team fails to carry out their duties diligently and professionally, the knock-on effect can have serious consequences. Take a look at the following response which will give you a good base from which to create your own.

"There are many people who form part of a doctor's team, and they are all just as important as each other. On a typical ward there will be senior or consultant doctor, the ward sister or charge nurse, the matron, nurses, other healthcare staff, admin staff and also medical students. As part of the wider team there will also be the ward cleaning team, patient transport staff and the paramedics. They are all as important as each other. Whilst there will be specific individuals who

work very closely with doctors, such as the senior nurse or matron, everyone is just as important if the organisation are to achieve their aim of delivering the highest standards of medical and patient care."

Q67. If successful and you graduate from medical school, which hospital or medical establishment would you like to work at and what do you know about their mission, vision and values?

This type of question is designed to see how far ahead you are planning and also whether or not you are aware of a medical establishment's important mission, vision and values. Take a look at the following sample response to this question which will assist you during your preparation.

"Although I would be more than happy to work anywhere as a qualified doctor, I would prefer to work at Tunbridge Wells Hospital which is based near Pembury. This particular Trust's mission is simply that their focus is their patients.

The vision of the Trust is to be a successful integrated healthcare provider in the top 20% of Trusts nationally for the quality of services which they deliver. They also have a certain number of dedicated values and these are that they always put the patient first, they will respect and value all patients, visitors and staff, take every opportunity to improve, aim to deliver high standards of quality and efficiency in everything they do and finally aim to achieve excellence by taking every opportunity to enhance their reputation.

I understand that if do eventually work at the hospital I will be required to abide by these important promises and statements."

Q68. What makes a good leader?

Doctors must have the ability to lead their team, and as such, you need to understand what actually makes a good leader. In order to become a good leader you must have a number of different skills that you can draw upon at a moment's notice and these include:

Being a visionary – An ability to see the end result or the desired goal

Provide inspiration – Great leaders need to be capable of inspiring their team towards a goal or objective

Strategic thinker – Being able to think outside of the box and plan for the future in line with the vision and mission of the medical organisation you are working for

Being liked by the team – Whilst not essential, it certainly helps to be liked by your team. If they like you, the will follow you

Being an effective decision maker – Having the ability to make decisions, even sometimes unpopular ones

Accepting of feedback and criticism - Good leaders should be able to take criticism from others. This will help them to continually improve

Whilst the above list is not exhaustive, it will provide you with a number of useful tips that will assist you during your preparation.

Q69. Do you have any weaknesses? If so, what are they?

Possibly the worst answer you can give for a question of this nature is that you don't have any weaknesses. Being able to identify that you have weaknesses is a strength in itself. It is important that you answer this question carefully as you could reduce your chances of getting a place in medical school if you portray yourself in a negative light. Whatever weakness you give, make sure you tell then panel what you are doing, or have already done to improve.

Here's an example of a response to this type of question:

"In a previous job I found it difficult to delegate work to others. I can be a bit of a perfectionist at times and I like a job or task to be done correctly to a high standard. Unfortunately this lack of trust caused problems within my team and a member of staff approached me to tell me they were not happy with the way I was working. I took their comments on-board and decided to ask the rest of the team if they felt the same.

The feedback I received was along the same lines; that the majority of people felt I should delegate more work and responsibility to them. Following this feedback I decided to change my style of approach and began to delegate more work, placing greater trust on my colleagues. This had a very positive effect and the workload increased dramatically as a result of this change. Morale within the team improved too and now I hold regular feedback meetings with my colleagues to see how we can improve.

I fully understand that if I am successful as a doctor I will need to learn to delegate and following this experience I am confident I will be able to do this."

This type of response identifies that you have a weakness, but also identifies a number of strengths. It shows that you have the ability to look at yourself and make changes where needed. Accepting constructive criticism is one thing, but doing something about it is another. This also leads on to another possible 'strength' quality in the fact that you can identify your weaknesses and do something about them.

Q70. As a qualified doctor how do you think you would communicate with your patients?

Perhaps a great way to approach communication with your patients as a doctor would be to follow these 3 stages:

STAGE 1 – INPUT

The input element of successful communication is where you listen and gather the facts. You will need to gather the facts in order to develop a process. Whilst listening to the patient you will need to employ effective listening skills, such as nodding and using expressions that demonstrate you are taking in all of the information offered.

STAGE 2 – PROCESS

During the process stage you will use the information gathered from the patient to make your decision on the best way forward. During the process you will also use your knowledge, skills and experiences to determine the most appropriate resolution.

STAGE 3 – OUTPUT

During the output stage you will communicate back to the patient using an appropriate style of communication that is suited to their needs. You will need to make sure your communication during stage 3 is both clear, concise and free from jargon so that the patient fully understands the way forward.

Q71. What is empathy and why is it important to the role of a doctor?

Here is sample response to help you with this question.

"I would describe empathy as being a multi-step process whereby the doctor's awareness of the patient's concerns produces a sequence of emotional engagement, compassion, and an urge to help the patient.

Empathy is a quality the doctor must possess naturally; it cannot be false. It is important to the role of a doctor as it will allow him or her to deliver outstanding patient care. If the patient feels that the doctor is not empathetic or understanding of their situation, patient care cannot be delivered. Most NHS Trust's will place patient care at the top of their mission.

If a doctor demonstrates empathy whenever applicable then he or she will go a long way to achieving the vision, mission and aims of the organisation. The doctor must also show empathy towards relatives of patients as the situation dictates. Empathy should not be confused with sympathy. Sympathy is 'concern for the welfare of the other', while empathy is the ability to appreciate the emotions and feelings of others"

Q72. As a doctor, how do you think you would you change your approach when talking to a child who arrived at hospital and was injured?

This is quite a tricky question to answer, especially as you are not yet qualified as a doctor. However, read the following tips which will give you some great pointers on how to deal with this type of situation.

- Get on same level as the child. This could be achieved by crouching or sitting down.

- Change vocabulary to suit the age of the child. This is of particular importance as it will make the child more responsive. If you talk in an authoritarian tone then this will probably make the child go into his/her shell.

- Consider using the child's favourite toy to make them feel more secure if the parents have brought it with them to hospital. There may also be some toys available at the hospital.

- Consider using the parents/guardian as reassurance and a communication aid.

- Start off by getting the child to explain the problem. Do not always act on the parent's assumptions, as these could be wrong.

- If child does not speak to you, consider asking the parents to get the answers to the questions for you.

- If appropriate, explain the actions that you are taking in order to reassure the child.

- Calm the parents down and demonstrate empathy when appropriate; this will calm the overall situation down and help them to assist you in dealing with the child.

Q73. Describe a situation at work where you have had to be flexible.

One of the key qualities required to become a doctor is that you are flexible. This means that you are flexible in terms of your availability and the shifts you will work. Doctors are often called to work at short notice and you will need to make yourself available, especially during unsociable hours and weekends.

In order for an NHS Trust or medical organisation to operate effectively, it needs people who do not want to work normal 9 – 5 hours. Many doctors say that one of the most frustrating aspects of their job is the instability of the life and the shift work. Obviously the medical school interview panel wants to know that this is not going to be a problem for you. Therefore, when responding to this type of question, you need to provide an example where you have already demonstrated commitment and flexibility to a previous or current role.

KEY AREAS TO CONSIDER:

- Demonstrate that your personal circumstances will allow for flexibility.

- Provide an example where you have gone out of your way to help a previous employer.

- Tell them that you understand how important flexible working is to the role of a doctor and within the medical profession as a whole.

Read the following sample response that follows.

"Whilst working in a previous role as a hairdresser, I was asked by my employer to work late every Saturday evening. The reason for this was that a number of clients could only make appointments between 6pm and 8pm on Saturday evenings.

Although I would usually go out on a Saturday night, I decided to agree to the additional hours. The salon was doing well and was beginning to get a very good reputation. I wanted to help the salon provide a high level of service to its customers and understood that if I didn't work late on those evenings they would lose the custom."

Q74. Stress can often be a big part of a doctors working life. How would you cope with stress?

There are many different coping mechanisms for stress in the workplace. During your response to this question you need to demonstrate that you are aware of the impact of stress on doctors and more importantly, the most effective ways to deal with it. Doctors will generally use two kinds of coping methods: those they are able to utilise at work, and those they used after work. Work-based coping strategies included things like talking with work colleagues, taking time out and using humour. One of the most effective work-based coping mechanisms is that of creating SMART goals –

Specific: A specific goal has a much greater chance of being accomplished than a general goal. To set a specific goal you must answer the six "W" questions:

Who: Who is involved?

What: What do I want to accomplish?

Where: Identify a location.

When: Establish a time-frame.

Which: Identify requirements and constraints.

Why: Specific reasons, purpose or benefits of accomplishing the goal.

Measurable: Establish concrete criteria for measuring progress toward the attainment of each goal you set. When you measure your progress, you stay on track, reach your target dates, and experience the exhilaration of achievement that spurs you on to continued effort required to reach your goal.

Attainable: When you identify goals that are most important to you, you begin to figure out ways you can make them come true. You develop the attitudes, abilities, skills, and financial capacity to reach them. You begin seeing previously overlooked opportunities to bring yourself closer to the achievement of your goals.

Realistic: To be realistic, a goal must represent an objective toward which you are both willing and able to work. Be sure that every goal represents substantial progress.

Timely: A goal should be completed within a time-frame. With no time frame there's no sense of urgency and the stress can build.

In addition at work-based coping strategies there are also strategies for outside of work, too. These include things like exercise, quiet-time, spending time with family, Yoga, Pilates, reading and swimming.

Q75. Have you ever lost your temper?

All of us have lost our temper at some point, but you need to be careful as to how much you disclose. Part of the role of a doctor is to remain calm under pressure and you need to demonstrate this in your response. The medical profession does not want to employ people who lose their temper at the slightest hint of stress or confrontation.

The question is designed to see how honest you are, and whether you are a naturally aggressive person. For a doctor to lose his or her temper would be both embarrassing and unprofessional.

KEY AREAS TO CONSIDER:

- Use 'non-confrontational' words and phrases during your response – patience, calm, understanding, empathy etc.

- Demonstrate your understanding of the doctor's role and the importance of remaining calm and professional whilst under pressure.

Take a look at the sample response that follows before taking the time to construct your own.

"In the whole I am a calm person and do not become aggressive or confrontational. Whilst it is only natural to be annoyed with people from time to time, I see no point in losing my temper. It is just wasted energy.

Doctor's cannot lose their temper with patients or other members of staff, it would be highly unprofessional. I appreciate that it must be frustrating at times dealing with pressurised situations, but the way to cope with them is to use appropriate mechanisms and strategies such as SMART."

Q76. What can you tell me about problem based (PBL)?

According to the British Medical Journal, problem based learning is where students use "triggers" from the problem case or scenario to define their own learning objectives. Subsequently they do independent, self-directed study before returning to the group to discuss and refine their acquired knowledge. Thus, PBL is not about problem solving per se, but rather it uses appropriate problems to increase knowledge and understanding. The process is clearly defined, and the several variations that exist all follow a similar series of steps.

Generic skills and attitudes gleaned from problem based learning include:

- Teamwork
- Chairing a group
- Listening
- Recording
- Cooperation
- Respect for colleagues' views
- Critical evaluation of literature
- Self-directed learning and use of resources
- Presentation skills

A sample case study where students will use PBL might be:

Mr Rogers is a 71year old man who lives in assisted accommodation on his own. His accommodation is a first floor apartment with one bedroom, a bathroom and a kitchen. There is a stair lift serving the first floor from the ground floor. He has a past medical history of angina and has recently been complaining about soreness in his knee joints which have prevented him from leaving the apartment.

During PBL students will go away individually and research triggers within the scenario before returning to the group to discuss their findings. For example, because Mr Rogers has been experiencing knee problems this may be a result of osteoarthritis. The students would then discuss the associated problems of Mr Rogers not being able to leave his apartment, such as mental health issues including depression.

Q77. What is the Hippocratic oath?

The Hippocratic oath is a long-standing tradition in medicine. Named after the Greek physician Hippocrates, the written oath was intended to act as a guideline for those entering the medical profession. Over the centuries, the exact wording has been modified and adapted, but the essence of the oath has remained the same. Doctors should respect those who have passed down medical knowledge and in turn pass their knowledge to the next generation. They should also respect the patients they are treating and ensure that they treat them to the best of their ability.

FURTHER GENERIC QUESTIONS TO PREPARE FOR DURING THE MEDICAL INTERVIEW

In this final section I will provide you with a further sample interview questions that you may wish to prepare for.

Q78. In addition to learning how to become a doctor, what else do you think you will gain from attending medical school?

Q79. There are limited places available at medical school and there are a number of applicants who have superior exam results to you. Why should we give you a place over them?

Q80. During a previous question you told us that you carry out regular research. Tell us about an important piece of current medical research that has caught your eye and why?

Q81. What are the pros and cons of being a doctor?

Q82. Do you think that nurses should take on more work in order to reduce the workload of doctors?

Q83. What is the difference between a day shift and a night shift in a typical hospital?

Q84. How do you think the NHS could be improved?

Q85. Do you think doctors and nurses should ever go on strike?

Q86. Do you think more people should opt for private healthcare? If so, why?

Q87. What's your view on how the media portray the medical profession and the NHS in general?

Q88. What are the leading causes of death in UK?

Q89. Tell us what you know about obesity and how you would prevent it?

Q90. Tell the interview panel what you know about organ-donation in the UK and we could get more people to become donors?

A FEW FINAL WORDS

You have now reached the end of the guide and no doubt you will be ready to start preparing for the medical interview. Just before you go off and start on your preparation, consider the following.

The majority of candidates who pass their medical interview have a number of common attributes. These are as follows:

1. They believe in themselves.

The first factor is self-belief. Regardless of what anyone tells you, you can become a doctor. Just like any job of this nature, you have to be prepared to work hard in order to be successful. Make sure you have the self-belief to pass the medical interview and fill your mind with positive thoughts.

2. They prepare fully.

The second factor is preparation. Those people who achieve in life prepare fully for every eventuality and that is what you must do when you are preparing for your medical interview. Work very hard and especially concentrate on your weak areas.

3. They persevere.

Perseverance is a fantastic word. Everybody comes across obstacles or setbacks in their life, but it is what you do about those setbacks that is important. If you fail at something, then ask yourself 'why' you have failed. This will allow you to improve for next time and if you keep improving and trying, success will eventually follow. Apply this same method of thinking when you apply to medical school.

4. They are self-motivated.

How much do you want a medical job? Do you want it, or do you really want it?

When you apply to medical school you should want it more than anything in the world. Your levels of self-motivation will shine through during your interview. For the weeks and months leading up to the interview, be motivated as best you can and always keep your fitness levels up as this will serve to increase your levels of motivation.

Work hard, stay focused and be what you want…

Richard McMunn

how2become

Visit www.how2become.com to find more titles and courses that will help you to pass any job interview or selection process:

- Online testing suites.
- Job interview DVDs and books.
- 1 day intensive career training courses.
- Psychometric testing books and CDs.

www.How2Become.com